# kidsource

super songs for church and school
compiled by **Capt. Alan Price, CA**

First published in Great Britain in 1999 by
KEVIN MAYHEW LIMITED
Buxhall
Stowmarket
Suffolk IP14 3DJ



The words of most of the songs and hymns in this publication are covered by a Church Copyright Licence which allows local church reproduction on overhead projector acetates, in service bulletins, songsheets, audio/visual recording and other formats. Full details of the licence are available from:

Christian Copyright Licensing Ltd
P.O. Box 1339
Eastbourne
East Sussex BN21 4YF
Telephone: 01323 417711, Ext. 229 Fax: 01323 417722

| | | |
|---|---|---|
| Words Only | ISBN | 1 84003 311 8 |
| | Catalogue No. | 1470151 |
| Full Music | ISBN | 1 84003 310 X |
| | ISMN | M 57004 506 8 |
| | Catalogue No. | 1470154 |

Cover illustration and design: Jonathan Stroulger
Typesetting: Richard Weaver

Printed and bound in Great Britain

# Foreword

*Christ's message in all its richness must live in your hearts. Teach and instruct each other with all wisdom. Sing psalms, hymns and sacred songs; sing to God with thanksgiving in your hearts.*

Colossians 3:16

Graham Kendrick started his preface in **the source,** the companion publication to this, with the same verse of scripture. It is with the same intent that we are pleased to introduce you to **kidsource**, this new collection of Christian songs with youngsters in mind.

Someone once said something like this: 'I don't mind the theology, as long as I can write the hymns'. The speaker was referring to the fact that many Christians seem to learn their theology from what they sing, rather than from any other source. For better or worse, it is the hymns and songs learnt in childhood that form the basis of faith for many.

Recent years have seen an 'explosion' of new music as much for children as for adults, yet in many churches the diet of music consists mainly of the hymns and songs of yesteryear. As good as many of them are, God has given so many new musical expressions of worship, which are much more relevant to this generation of children. There have been other collections, but, as with **the source**, we have sought to bring together as wide a range of songs as possible. There were many from which we had to choose, and often the choice was difficult.

Songs for children may be simpler and may have a high 'fun' content, but it is our conviction that whatever theological content they have should be good and biblically sound. We have sought to include hymns and songs that are primarily child-friendly, with good, memorable tunes, and words that express the Christian faith in terms that children can 'own'. There are one or two songs with an occasional grammatical 'slip-up', but they are still included because they are already popular with children and their leaders. There are also those that some might term 'adult' worship songs, but these have been included as those proven to be as accessible to children as to adults in their expression of faith and worship. It is also our belief that many adults will also find these 'children's' songs to be singable without any 'cringe-factor', thus being a collection providing a good resource for all-age worship.

Music is a major part of life, especially for children. Apart from the almost constant 'background music' surrounding them, the educational value of music is well known as a means of reinforcing teaching. However, music is also a vital means of expressing response to God and his message. Thus **kidsource** has songs suitable for reinforcing biblical teaching on a wide range of topics, and also those songs which will enable children to express their worship and adoration and their desire to follow the Friend and Saviour, Jesus Christ.

CAPT. ALAN PRICE, CA
Compiler

JONATHAN BUGDEN
Adviser

## 1 Paul Crouch and David Mudie

2 - 4 - 6 - 8, come and join the dance
and celebrate. Jesus!
1 - 3 - 5 - 7, let's all join in praising
heaven's high King. Jesus!

1 - 2 - 3 - 4, who's that knocking at the
door of your heart? Jesus!
5 - 6 - 7 - 8, open up your life before
it's too late. Jesus!

He'll multiply your blessings and take
your blues away.
His love heals our divisions and adds
value to each day.



## 2 Ian Smale

5 0 0 0 + hungry folk,
5 0 0 0 + hungry folk,
5 0 0 0 + hungry folk
came 4 2 listen 2 Jesus.
The 6 x 2 said O O O,
the 6 x 2 said O O O,
the 6 x 2 said O O O,
where can I get some food from?

Just 1 had 1 2 3 4 5,
just 1 had 1 2 3 4 5,
just 1 had 1 2 3 4 5
loaves and 1 2 fishes.
When Jesus blessed the 5 + 2,
when Jesus blessed the 5 + 2,
when Jesus blessed the 5 + 2
they were increased many x over.

5 0 0 0 + 8 it up,
5 0 0 0 + 8 it up,
5 0 0 0 + 8 it up
with 1 2 3 4 5 6 7 8 9 10 11 12
basketfuls left over.



## 3 Dave Bilbrough

Abba, Father, let me be
yours and yours alone.
May my will for ever be
more and more your own.
Never let my heart grow cold,
never let me go.
Abba, Father, let me be
yours and yours alone.



## 4 Noel and Tricia Richards

All heav'n declares
the glory of the risen Lord.
Who can compare
with the beauty of the Lord?
For ever he will be
the Lamb upon the throne.
I gladly bow the knee
and worship him alone.

I will proclaim
the glory of the risen Lord.
Who once was slain
to reconcile us to God.
For ever you will be
the Lamb upon the throne.
I gladly bow the knee
and worship you alone.



## 5 Graham Kendrick

All I once held dear,
built my life upon,
all this world reveres,
and wars to own,
all I once thought gain
I have counted loss;
spent and worthless now,
compared to this.

*Continued overleaf*

*Knowing you, Jesus, knowing you,*
*there is no greater thing.*
*You're my all, you're the best,*
*you're my joy, my righteousness,*
*and I love you, Lord.*

Now my heart's desire
is to know you more,
to be found in you
and known as yours.
To possess by faith
what I could not earn,
all-surpassing gift
of righteousness.

Oh, to know the pow'r
of your risen life,
and to know you in your sufferings.
To become like you
in your death, my Lord,
so with you to live
and never die.



## 6 Doug Marks-Smircich

All of my heart, all of my soul,
all of my mind, all of my strength.
All of my heart, all of my soul,
all of my mind, all of my strength.

With ev'rything within me
I want to praise you, Lord.
I want to love you with all that I am,
and bring joy to your heart.

With ev'rything within me
I want to praise you, Lord.
I want to love you with all that I am,
and bring joy to your heart.
Let me bring joy to your heart
all of my life.



## 7 Paul Crouch and David Mudie

All the creatures of the earth
will declare that you are King.
Ev'ry woman, man and child
confess you Lord of ev'rything.
All creation with one voice,
ev'ry galaxy and star,
in adoration will proclaim
what a holy God you are.

Ev'ry person will bow down,
ev'ry eye will see your face.
When your glory fills the sky,
you will be seen in ev'ry place.
All the people of the world,
ev'rybody near and far,
in adoration will proclaim
what a holy God you are.



## 8 Cecil Frances Alexander

*All things bright and beautiful,*
*all creatures great and small,*
*all things wise and wonderful,*
*the Lord God made them all.*

Each little flow'r that opens,
each little bird that sings,
he made their glowing colours,
he made their tiny wings.

The purple-headed mountain,
the river running by,
the sunset and the morning,
that brightens up the sky.

The cold wind in the winter,
the pleasant summer sun,
the ripe fruits in the garden,
he made them ev'ry one.

He gave us eyes to see them,
and lips that we may tell
how great is God Almighty,
who has made all things well.

## 9 John Newton

Amazing grace! How sweet the sound
that saved a wretch like me.
I once was lost, but now I'm found;
was blind, but now I see.

'Twas grace that taught my heart to fear,
and grace my fears relieved.
How precious did that grace appear
the hour I first believed.

Through many dangers, toils and snares
I have already come.
'Tis grace that brought me safe thus far,
and grace will lead me home.

The Lord has promised good to me,
his word my hope secures;
he will my shield and portion be
as long as life endures.

When we've been there a thousand
  years,
bright shining as the sun,
we've no less days to sing God's praise
than when we first begun.

## 10 Karen Porter

A million stars are in the sky,
how great is God, how small am I.
This vast expanse, at his command,
and yet my future is in his hands.

*He is so great,*
*he is so mighty,*
*and yet he cares*
*for someone like me.*
*He is so great,*
*he is so mighty,*
*eternal God and Father is he!*

Great King of kings, he reigns on high,
ruler of earth, and sea and sky.
A tiny bird falls from a tree,
God sees it all, and he knows me.

He sent his own Son to save me,
he died so I could be free.
He is so great . . .

*Eternal God and Father is he!*



## 11 J. W. Wood

And God said the sun should shine,
the rain should fall, the flowers should
  grow;
and God said the birds should sing,
and it was so, was so.

And God said the grass should grow,
the trees bear fruits, the winds should
  blow;
and God said the streams should flow,
and it was so, was so.



## 12 Jim Bailey

As for me and my house,
as for me and my family,
as for me and my children,
we will serve the Lord.
As for me and my house,
as for me and my family,
as for me and my children,
we will serve the Lord.

*Continued overleaf*

In this family,
we're gonna do things properly,
read God's word ev'ry day
and then we'll try to pray;
although we get it wrong,
we will still carry on,
make Jesus number one
in this place.
In this place we're gonna say grace.

As for me and my house,
as for me and my family,
as for me and my children,
we will serve the Lord.
As for me and my house,
as for me and my family,
as for me and my children,
we will serve the Lord.



## 13 Paul Crouch and David Mudie

As we share bread in the family of God,
we think of Jesus, God's Son.
Died in our place as the payment for sin.
We adore you and worship you now.

*Jesus, our Saviour,*
*ruler in power,*
*we come now*
*and give you our praise.*
(Repeat)

As we share wine in the family of God,
we think of Jesus, God's Son.
Rose from the dead in victory and
power.
We adore you and worship you now.



## 14 William Chatterton Dix alt. Roger Jones

As with gladness men of old
did the guiding star behold,
as with joy they hailed its light,
leading onward beaming bright.

*So, most gracious God, may we*
*evermore be led to thee.*

As with joyful steps they sped
to that lowly manger bed,
there to bend the knee before
him whom heav'n and earth adore.

As they offered gifts most rare,
at that manger rude and bare,
so may we with holy joy
pure and free from sin's alloy.

Holy Jesus, ev'ry day
keep us in the narrow way,
and when earthly things are past
save our ransomed souls at last.



## 15 William James Kirkpatrick

Away in a manger,
no crib for a bed,
the little Lord Jesus
laid down his sweet head.
The stars in the bright sky
looked down where he lay,
the little Lord Jesus,
asleep on the hay.

The cattle are lowing,
the baby awakes,
but little Lord Jesus
no crying he makes.
I love thee, Lord Jesus!
Look down from the sky,
and stay by my side
until morning is nigh.

Be near me, Lord Jesus;
I ask thee to stay
close by me for ever,
and love me, I pray.
Bless all the dear children
in thy tender care,
and fit us for heaven,
to live with thee there.

## 16 Paul Field

A wiggly, waggly worm, a slipp'ry, slimy slug,
a creepy, crawly, buzzy thing, a tickly, wickly bug;
of all the things to be, I'm happy that I'm me.
Thank you, Lord, I'm happy that I'm me.
I'm happy that I'm me, happy that I'm me.
There's no one else in all the world that I would rather be.
A wiggly, waggly worm, a slippery, slimy slug,
a creepy, crawly, buzzy thing, a tickly, wickly bug.

A prickly porcupine, a clumsy kangaroo,
a croaky frog, a hairy hog, a monkey in a zoo;
of all the things to be, I'm happy that I'm me.
Thank you, Lord, I'm happy that I'm me.
I'm happy that I'm me, happy that I'm me.
There's no one else in all the world that I would rather be.
A prickly porcupine, a clumsy kangaroo,
a croaky frog, a hairy hog, a monkey in a zoo.



## 17 Morris Chapman

Be bold, be strong,
for the Lord, your God, is with you.
Be bold, be strong,
for the Lord, your God, is with you.
I am not afraid, I am not dismayed,
because I'm walking in faith and victory,
come on and walk in faith and victory,
for the Lord, your God, is with you.



## 18 Capt. Alan Price, CA

Because of who he is,
because of who he is,
because of all he's done,
because of all he's done,
because of all his love for us,
we worship the Three in One.

We have come to God the Father,
we have come to God the Father,
in the name of God the Son,
in the name of God the Son,
by the power of the Spirit,
we worship the Three in One.

Because of who you are,
because of who you are,
because of all you've done,
because of all you've done,
because of all your love for us,
we worship the Three in One.

## 19 David J. Evans

Be still, for the presence of the Lord,
the Holy One is here.
Come, bow before him now,
with reverence and fear.
In him no sin is found,
we stand on holy ground.
Be still, for the presence of the Lord,
the Holy One is here.

Be still, for the glory of the Lord
is shining all around;
he burns with holy fire,
with splendour he is crowned.
How awesome is the sight,
our radiant King of light!
Be still, for the glory of the Lord
is shining all around.

Be still, for the power of the Lord
is moving in this place;
he comes to cleanse and heal,
to minister his grace.
No work too hard for him,
in faith receive from him.
Be still, for the power of the Lord
is moving in this place.



## 20 Capt. Alan Price, CA

Be the centre of my life, Lord Jesus,
be the centre of my life I pray;
be my Saviour to forgive me,
be my friend to be with me,
be the centre of my life today!

Let the power of your presence, Lord Jesus,
from the centre of my life shine through;
oh, let ev'rybody know it,
I really want to show it,
that the centre of my life is you!



## 21 Judy Bailey

Calling on the Spirit (calling on the Spirit),
Holy Spirit (Holy Spirit),
come down to us (come down to us)
in fire and rain (in fire and rain).
Fire brings us holiness (fire brings us holiness),
purity and passion (purity and passion),
rain revives us (rain revives us),
gives us hope again.

*We've been waiting, now's the time,*
*hear our hearts, hear our cry.*
*Let the Spirit move on ev'ryone,*
*let the fire fall, let the rain come down.*
*Let the fire fall, and let the rain come;*
*let the fire fall, and let the rain come;*
*let the fire fall, and let the rain come down.*



## 22 Capt. Alan Price, CA

*Can we love one another*
*just like Jesus has loved us,*
*can we do what he commands?*
*Can we love other people*
*just as we love ourselves,*
*or is it just too much to demand?*

Yes, we can and we will!
yes, we can and we will!
even if sometimes it's hard.
Yes, we can and we will!
yes, we can and we will!
even if sometimes it's hard.

Yes, we can and we will!
yes, we can and we will!
even if sometimes we fail and let him down.
Yes, we can and we will!
yes, we can and we will!
even if sometimes we fail.

Yes, we can and we will!
yes, we can and we will!
even if sometimes we fail and let him down.
Yes, we can and we will!
yes, we can and we will!
even if sometimes we fail
(God will help us).
We will love one another
just like Jesus has loved us,
and we will do what he commands!



## 23 Paul Field

Can you count the stars shining in the sky?
Can you hold the moonlight in your hand?
Can you stop the waves rolling on the shore?
Or find the place where rainbows meet the land?

*I've got a friend who knows*
*how all these things are done.*
*Jesus, Lord of all, God's only Son.*

Up in outer space, planets spinning round,
millions more than we can ever see.
It's hard to understand how God, who made it all,
still cares about someone like you and me.



## 24 Graham Kendrick

Can you see what we have made
for this very special day?
An orange for our planet home
circling around the sun.

Count the seasons as we sing,
summer, autumn, winter, spring.
Sing to God who sends the rain,
making all things new again.

*Candle light, burning bright,*
*chase the darkness of the night.*
*Christ the light, light our way,*
*live inside our hearts today.*

See the food with colours bright,
tastebuds tingle at the sight.
Let's be thankful as we share,
God's good gifts are ev'rywhere.

Why then is the world we made,
wrapped around with ribbon red?
Red is for the ransom paid,
when our Lord was crucified.

There's a world I'm dreaming of,
where there's peace and joy and love.
Light of Jesus ev'rywhere,
this is my Christingle prayer.



## 25 Gary Oliver

Celebrate Jesus, celebrate!
Celebrate Jesus, celebrate!
Celebrate Jesus, celebrate!
Celebrate Jesus, celebrate!
He is risen, he is risen,
and he lives for evermore.
He risen, he is risen,
come on and celebrate
the resurrection of our Lord.



## 26 Capt. Alan Price, CA

*Christmas, it's Christmas,*
*it's Christmas once again.*
*The birthday of Jesus,*
*born in Bethlehem.*

*Continued overleaf*

The Lord, who was that tiny baby,
existed long before the birth.
He laid aside his heav'nly glory
to be Jesus, Saviour of the earth!

*Christmas, it's Christmas,*
*it's Christmas once again.*
*The birthday of Jesus,*
*born in Bethlehem.*

The Lord, who was that tiny baby,
grew up and lived to show the Father's love.
He laid aside his life to bring us back to God,
raised to life, he's back in heaven above.

*Christmas, it's Christmas,*
*it's Christmas once again.*
*We thank you, Lord Jesus,*
*that you came. Amen.*



## 27 Robyn Barnett

Church is not a building,
it's the people there inside;
people who love Jesus
and wear his badge with pride.
Though he's gone to heaven,
he's left us in his place,
to be his body here on earth,
his hands, his feet, his face . . .



## 28 Paul Crouch and David Mudie

C - L - A - P, clap my hands.
J - U - M - P, jump!
Yes, yes, S - T - A - M - P my feet,
for J - E - S - U - S!
Jesus is the B - E - S - T friend that you could know.
He will always be with you, wherever you G - O.



## 29 Tom Daniel, Bob Buzbee, Ernie Rettino, Debbie Kerner

*Clap your hands, stomp your feet,*
*spread the love of Jesus to ev'ryone you meet.*
*Oh! Clap your hands, stomp your feet,*
*spread a little love around.*

The love of Jesus is a sweet, sweet song,
that you can give to others as you walk along.
With a smile on your face, and his love in your heart,
you spread the love of Jesus, now everybody start to

The love of Jesus is a miracle
God has given ev'ry boy and girl.
His Son came to earth because he loves us so,
and now it's up to us to let his miracle show. Oh!

## 30 Yvonne Scott

Come along, ev'ryone, let's worship God
together.
Come along, ev'ryone, let's worship God
together.
Ev'ry girl, ev'ry boy, let's worship God
together.
Praise, praise, praise, praise, praise
together.



## 31 Mark and Helen Johnson

*Come and join in the song,*
*Jesus Christ is Lord over all,*
*and he lives to reign for evermore.*
*The heavens applaud: 'He's alive!*
*He's alive!'*

*Lift your hearts and your voices,*
*fill the earth with rejoicing for*

He's ascended to the skies,
in heaven now he reigns.
Lord of glory, Lord of life,
he will return again.

Ev'ry knee shall bow to him,
and ev'ryone confess:
Jesus Christ is Lord and King,
he's conquered sin and death!

Ev'ry nation, ev'ry tribe
will glorify his name.
All creation shall bow down
and honour him with praise!

*Come and join in the song,*
*Jesus Christ is Lord over all,*
*and he lives to reign for evermore.*
*The heavens applaud: 'He's alive!*
*He's alive! He's alive! He's alive!'*



## 32 Mike Burn

Come and sing, come and sing,
come and sing to Jesus now.
Come and sing, come and sing,
come and sing to Jesus now.
Give him thanks for who he is,
give him thanks for what he's done,
come and sing.

*Jesus won it all for us*
*when he shed his blood on the cross.*
*Sin and death were swallowed up,*
*they don't have a hold on us now,*
*that's the reason to sing.*

Come and dance, come and dance,
come and dance for Jesus now.
Come and dance, come and dance,
come and dance for Jesus now.
Dance for joy before the throne,
let your inhibitions go,
come and dance.



## 33 Chris Jackson

Come, Jesus, come,
touch my heart with a deep compassion.
Lord, I want to see,
I want to feel what you feel.
Fill me with love,
fill me with pow'r,
send your Holy Spirit.
Come, Lord Jesus, come.

## 34 Patricia Morgan and Dave Bankhead

Come on and celebrate
his gift of love, we will celebrate
the Son of God who loved us
and gave us life.
We'll shout your praise, O King,
you give us joy nothing else can bring,
we'll give to you our offering
in celebration praise.

Come on and celebrate, celebrate,
celebrate and sing,
celebrate and sing to the King.
Come on and celebrate, celebrate,
celebrate and sing,
celebrate and sing to the King.



## 35 Ian White

Crackers and turkeys and pudding and
cream,
toys in the windows that I've never seen.
This is the Christmas that ev'ryone sees,
but Christmas means more to me.

*It's somebody's birthday I won't forget,*
*as I open the things that I get.*
*I'll remember the inn and the stable so*
*bare,*
*and Jesus who once lay there.*

Ev'ryone's out shopping late ev'ry night,
for candles and presents and Christmas
tree lights.
This is the Christmas that ev'ryone sees,
but Christmas means more to me.

Christmas morning, the start of the day,
there's presents to open and new games
to play.
This is the Christmas that ev'ryone sees,
but Christmas means more to me.



## 36 Ian Smale

Dear Lord, my Father who's in heav'n,
honoured be your holy name.
May your kingdom come,
may your will be done,
here on earth as it is in heav'n.
Dear Lord, please give us food today,
and forgive us as we forgive others.
May your testing be not too hard to bear,
and deliver us from the evil one.
Amen, amen, amen, amen.
Amen, amen, amen, amen.



## 37 Doug Horley

*Do not worry, oh, do not worry, oh,*
*do not worry, oh, 'bout anything.*
*(Repeat)*

Do not worry about anything
but pray and ask God for ev'rything you
need,
and when you pray, oh,
always give thanks
and the peace of God will keep your
mind in Jesus.

Does worry ever stop bad things
happening?
No, and it won't help make them go away.
Will worry ever, ever, ever help you get
better
when you're really, really, really, really
sick? No way!
Worry won't help when the going gets
tough,
worry won't help when life is really rough,
but instead of prayin' last and panicking
fast,
don't worry in a hurry, turn to Jesus,
turn to Jesus, turn to Jesus. Oh, turn to
Jesus.

## 38 Sammy Horner

*Don't be afraid or put off,*
*just trust with all your might,*
*stand up, speak out*
*and live for the things of God.*
*So if you're scared, or let down,*
*just learn from what's gone on,*
*stand up, speak out*
*and live for the things of God.*

Doesn't matter if you're young or old,
or if you're rich or poor;
there's no easy way to live for God,
of that you can be sure.

Doesn't matter if you're big or small,
strong or insecure;
there's no easy way to live for God,
of that you can be sure.



## 39 Nick Harding

*Don't be an actor, don't be a fraud,*
*'cos you might fool others*
*but you won't fool the Lord.*
*Don't be a show-off, don't do an act,*
*'cos it's your heart, heart, heart that matters,*
*and that's a fact!*

You can dress up smart, you can dress up rough,
you can try to act big, you can try to act tough,
but after a while you'll have had enough,
and what good would that do?

You can act happy when you're feeling down,
you can put on a smile when your face wants to frown,
you know it's no use trying to be a clown,
just be the real 'you'.



## 40 Karen Lafferty

Don't build your house on the sandy land,
don't build it too near the shore.
Well, it might look kind of nice,
but you'll have to build it twice,
oh, you'll have to build your house once more.
You'd better * build your house upon a rock,
make a good foundation on a solid spot.
Oh, the storms may come and go,
but the peace of God you will know.

**If sung as a round the second group of voices enters here.*



## 41 Ralph Chambers

Don't know much about the ozone layer,
rain forests seem miles away,
but each of us can be a player,
fight to save the world God has made.
This is God's world, this is God's world,
and you're a member of the human race.
This is God's world, this is God's world,
let's try to make it a better place.

## 42 Merrilyn Billing

Don't repay evil for evil,
don't snap back at those
who say unkind things about you.
*(Repeat)*

Instead, pray, pray for God's help for them,
for we are to be kind to others.
Pray, pray for God's help for them,
and God will bless us for it.

Pray, pray for God's help for them,
for we are to be kind to others.
Pray, pray for God's help for them,
and God will bless us for it.



## 43 Judy MacKenzie Dunn

*Don't you worry about tomorrow,*
*where you'll be or what you'll say.*
*He'll take care of your tomorrow*
*if you just follow him today.*

Where shall I go, what should I say,
how do I know which is the way?
Facing the future, feeling afraid,
time to remember what Jesus said.

When days are dark and nights are long,
when times are hard and things go wrong,
he'll never leave you, he won't let you
down,
he's there to lead you to solid ground.



## 44 Paul Field

Down in the jungle on a Saturday night,
all the animals get together,
to talk about the things that man has
done
to change the world for ever.
The wonders of creation die
from greed and from pollution,
if man's supposed to be so smart
then where is the solution?
All things bright and beautiful,
all creatures great and small,
but the trouble with man just seems to be
he doesn't care at all.

When God made ev'ry living thing
he made the world for sharing.
He wants us all to get along
by loving and by caring.
A perfect earth for ev'ryone
that we should be enjoying,
so how is it that we have come
to spoiling and destroying?
All things wise and wonderful,
the Lord God made them all.
The trouble with man just seems to be
that he won't share at all.

The trouble with me and the trouble
with you,
we want so much that we don't need,
sooner or later we've got to see
and live together, like it's meant to be.



## 45 Mark and Helen Johnson

Easter jubilation fills the streets and
towns,
celebrations have begun.
Hear the music and the dancing now,
join the laughter and the fun!

*Oh, raise a joyful shout!*
*Clap your hands and dance,*
*let your feelings out.*
*Oh, hear what it's about:*
*Christ, the Lord, has come*
*to set us free. *Hoy!*

Put aside your sorrows, wipe your tears away,
for a better time will come.
There's a promise of a better day,
join the laughter and the fun!

La, la, la, la, la, etc.

Easter jubilation fills the streets and towns,
celebrations have begun.
Hear the music and the dancing now,
join the laughter and the fun!

* Last time only



## 46 Doug Horley

*Ev'rybody has a wobble from time to time,*
*ev'rybody has some shake, rattle and roll in their lives.*
*Ev'rybody has a wobble from time to time,*
*ev'rybody has some shake, rattle and roll in their lives.*

It's not wrong to have some questions,
it's not wrong to have some doubts,
but sometimes we need help
from our friends to work things out.
To the promises he's made us,
we must learn to hold on tight,
'cos no way will he leave us,
even in the darkest night.



## 47 Ian Smale

*Ev'ry day with Jesus,*
*ev'ry day with Jesus,*
*ev'ry day with Jesus,*
*I want to spend my ev'ry day with him.*

I realise the Bible is a book I need to read,
it shows me how my Christian life can start.
Then as I get older, just like a healthy food,
it strengthens me when I hide it in my heart.

I realise the Bible is a book I need to read,
and ev'ry page I read I know is true.
For God has breathed upon his book to help me ev'ry day,
and show me what's his plan for me to do.

I realise the Bible is a book I need to read,
the more I read the more I'm going to know,
about things of importance and how my life should be,
it's what a Christian needs to make things grow.



## 48 Ian White

*Ev'rywhere he walks with me,*
*and through prayer he talks with me.*
*He has cared enough for me,*
*to die, to set me free.*

Since then you have been raised with Christ,
set your hearts on things above.
Where Christ is seated at God's right hand,
set your minds on things above.

*Continued overleaf*

*Ev'rywhere he walks with me,*
*and through prayer he talks with me.*
*He has cared enough for me,*
*to die, to set me free.*

Put to death whatever is sin,
rid yourself of all these things.
You have been renewed in the Lord,
and he is all, and is in all.

Let his peace now rule in your hearts.
Let his Word be rich in you.
Sing psalms and hymns with thanks to
God,
praise him in all that you do.



## 49 Graham Kendrick

Far and near hear the call,
worship him, Lord of all;
families of nations, come,
celebrate what God has done.

Deep and wide is the love
heaven sent from above;
God's own Son, for sinners died,
rose again – he is alive.

*Say it loud, say it strong,*
*tell the world what God has done;*
*say it loud, praise his name,*
*let the earth rejoice –*
*for the Lord reigns.*

At his name, let praise begin;
oceans roar, nature sing,
for he comes to judge the earth
in righteousness and in his truth.



## 50 Capt. Alan Price, CA

Father God, I come to you
and wonder at your love,
that you knew me,
and you cared for me
before the world was made;
and I stand and think
and love to feel
your love so deep inside,
and to know for sure
your love for me
will never, ever fade.



## 51 Yvonne Scott

Father God, I know you love me so,
Father God, I know you care for me.
Father God, I know you love me so,
Father God, I'm small but you care
for me.

Father God, I'm small but I love you so,
Father God, I'm small but I'll follow you.
Father God, I'm small but I love you so,
Father God, I'm small but I'll follow you.



## 52 Ian Smale

Father God, I wonder
how I managed to exist
without the knowledge of your
parenthood
and your loving care.
But now I am your child,
I am adopted in your family
and I can never be alone
'cause, Father God, you're there beside
me.

I will sing your praises,
I will sing your praises,
I will sing your praises,
for evermore.
I will sing your praises,
I will sing your praises,
I will sing your praises,
for evermore.



## 53 Paul Crouch and David Mudie

Father God, you love me and you know me inside out.
You know the words that I will say before I speak them out.
You are all around me, you hold me in your hand.
Your love for me is more than I can ever understand.

Father God, from your love there is nowhere I can hide.
If I go down into the depths or cross the ocean wide,
there your love would find me, you'd take me in your hand.
Your love for me is more than I can ever understand.



## 54 Danny Daniels

Father, I can call you Father,
for I am your child
today, tomorrow and always,
you are my Father.

Father, how I love you,
Father, I will sing your praise,
today, tomorrow and always,
for you're my Father.

*Father, Father, Father, to me.*
*Father, holy Father, Father to me.*

Father, I will serve you,
Father, I will seek your face
today, tomorrow and always,
you are my Father.



## 55 Judy Bailey and Dave Bankhead

Father, I do adore you,
worship before you,
I love you, Lord.
*(Repeat)*

*You have opened up my eyes*
*to see such beauty in your face,*
*a love that cared enough to set me free;*
*and my heart is filled with wonder*
*at the glory of your grace,*
*I'm so thankful, Lord,*
*that now you live in me.*

Jesus, I do adore you . . .

Spirit, I do adore you . . .



## 56 Yvonne Scott

Father, I thank you with my voice,
la-la-la, la-la-la.
Father, I thank you with my voice,
with my voice.

Father, I thank you with my hands,
with my hands, with my hands.
Father, I thank you with my hands,
with my hands.
*(Each time the words 'with my hands' are sung, then clap hands)*

*Continued overleaf*

Father, I thank you with my feet,
with my feet, with my feet.
Father, I thank you with my feet,
with my feet.
*(Each time the words 'with my feet' are sung, then jump or dance)*

Father, I thank you with my voice,
with my hands, with my feet.
Father, I thank you with my voice,
hands and feet.
*('With my voice' – no action, 'with my hands' – clap, 'with my feet' – jump/dance)*



## 57 Terrye Coelho

Father, we adore you,
lay our lives before you,
how we love you.

Jesus, we adore you . . .

Spirit, we adore you . . .

## 58 Paul Crouch and David Mudie

Father, your word is like a light in the darkness.
Father, your word is like a sharp, sharp sword.
Father, your word is like a stream in the desert.
There's nothing that compares with the wisdom of your word.



## 59 Paul Field

Find the silence through the noise,
listen to the Saviour's voice,
he is calling you, calling you to come.
Don't turn away, don't close your eyes,
you need his love to fill your life.
He is calling you, calling you to come.
He is reaching out to be by your side,
he will be your friend for life.

*Give him your heart, give him your heart.*
*You will find out that life really starts when you give him your heart.*

You may be good, you may be bad,
you may be happy, you may be sad,
still he is calling you,
calling you to come.
Find the silence through the noise,
listen to the Saviour's voice,
he is calling you,
calling you to come.
He is reaching out to be by your side,
he will be your friend for life.



## 60 Nick Harding

*For ever I will live my life by faith;*
*I'm always gonna live my life by faith.*
*For ever I will live my life by faith;*
*I'm always gonna live my life by faith.*

By faith I can obey,
by faith I praise and pray,
by faith I am made new,
by faith I know it's true.

By faith I take God's hand,
by faith I understand,
by faith I am made pure,
by faith I can be sure.

## 61 Dave Richards

For I'm building a people of power
and I'm making a people of praise,
that will move through this land by my
Spirit,
and will glorify my precious name.
Build your church, Lord,
make us strong, Lord,
join our hearts, Lord,
through your Son.
Make us one, Lord, in your body,
in the kingdom of your Son.



## 62 Graham Kendrick

From heav'n you came, helpless babe,
entered our world, your glory veiled;
not to be served but to serve,
and give your life that we might live.

*This is our God, the Servant King,*
*he calls us now to follow him,*
*to bring our lives as a daily offering*
*of worship to the Servant King.*

There in the garden of tears,
my heavy load he chose to bear;
his heart with sorrow was torn.
'Yet not my will but yours,' he said.

Come, see his hands and his feet,
the scars that speak of sacrifice,
hands that flung stars into space,
to cruel nails surrendered.

So let us learn how to serve,
and in our lives enthrone him;
each other's needs to prefer,
for it is Christ we're serving.



## 63 Richard Hubbard

F - U - N - E - N - R - G?
Come and praise the Lord with me.
O - I - C - Y - M - 2 - B
filled with joy and victor - E.
F - U - N - E - N - R - G?
S - V - F - Z - N - R - G.
J - E - S - U - S for me,
S - S - Y - I - M so 3.

F - U - F - N - 10 - E bounce,
& U - F - N - 10 - E go,
come 2 J - E - S - U - S,
E - L give U zap 2 glow.
O - I - 8 - 2 - C - U sad,
& I - 8 - 2 - C - U low,
U - C - U - R - O - K 2 God,
& E wants 2 - C - U grow!

*The interpretation*

Have you any energy?
Come and praise the Lord with me.
Oh, I see why I'm to be
filled with joy and victory.
Have you any energy?
'Yes, we have the energy.'
J - E - S - U - S for me,
this is why I am so free.

If you haven't any bounce,
and you haven't any go,
come to J - E - S - U - S,
he will give you zap to glow.
Oh, I hate to see you sad,
and I hate to see you low,
you see you are OK to God,
and he wants to see you grow!

## 64 Capt. Alan Price, CA

Get on board! the Kingdom train is moving.
Get on board! hear the whistle blow.
Get on board! if you want to follow Jesus,
sh, sh, woo woo, it's time to go.
Woo woo! we'll keep on moving.
Woo woo! to the journey's end.
Woo woo! by the power of the Spirit,
we're travelling with Jesus on the Kingdom train.

*Last time*
We're travelling with Jesus,
we're travelling with Jesus,
we're travelling with Jesus on the Kingdom train.



## 65 Jim Bailey

Give me a heart of compassion,
give me a hope for the lost.
Give me a passion for those
who are broken and down.
Lord, I am ready and willing
to serve the weak and the young.
Help me to put into action
the words of this song.

*And enable your servants,*
*enable your servants to preach good news,*
*to preach good news.*
*(Repeat)*

I'll sing the songs of salvation,
boldly I'll speak out your word.
I'll let them know by my life,
I will show you are Lord.
I'll tell them all about Jesus,
I'll tell them all about you,
I'm not ashamed of the gospel
or what it can do.

We're moving forward together,
as one voice boldly proclaim,
the old and the young will be strong,
and we'll lift up your name
on to the streets to the people,
ev'ry man, woman and child,
and as we go you are with us,
you've given your pow'r.

*You've enabled your servants . . .*



## 66 Traditional

Give me oil in my lamp, keep me burning.
Give me oil in my lamp, I pray.
Give me oil in my lamp, keep me burning,
keep me burning till the break of day.

*Sing hosanna, sing hosanna,*
*sing hosanna to the King of kings!*
*Sing hosanna, sing hosanna,*
*sing hosanna to the King!*

Give me joy in my heart, keep me singing.
Give me joy in my heart, I pray.
Give me joy in my heart, keep me singing,
keep me singing till the break of day.

Give me love in my heart, keep me serving.
Give me love in my heart, I pray.
Give me love in my heart, keep me serving,
keep me serving till the break of day.

Give me peace in my heart, keep me resting.
Give me peace in my heart, I pray.
Give me peace in my heart, keep me resting,
keep me resting till the break of day.

## 67 Yvonne Scott

Gives! Gives! Gives!
That's what God does.
Gives! Gives! Gives!
That's what God does each day.
Great! Great! Great!
God is very great.

Thanks! Thanks! Thanks!
That's what we say.
Thanks! Thanks! Thanks!
That's what we say each day.
Great! Great! Great!
God is very great.



## 68 Henry Smith

Give thanks with a grateful heart.
Give thanks to the Holy One.
Give thanks because he's given
Jesus Christ, his Son.
Give thanks with a grateful heart.
Give thanks to the Holy One.
Give thanks because he's given
Jesus Christ, his Son.

And now let the weak say, 'I am strong',
let the poor say, 'I am rich',
because of what the Lord has done for us.
And now let the weak say, 'I am strong',
let the poor say, 'I am rich',
because of what the Lord has done for us.

Give thanks.



## 69 Danny Daniels

Glory, glory in the highest;
glory to the Almighty;
glory to the Lamb of God,
and glory to the living Word;
glory to the Lamb!
*(Repeat)*
I give glory (glory),
glory (glory),
glory, glory to the Lamb!
I give glory (glory),
glory (glory),
glory, glory to the Lamb!
I give glory to the Lamb!



## 70 Capt. Alan Price, CA

God always has time for us,
he will always listen.
God always has time for us,
time for evr'yone.
He cares for you
and he cares for me,
he isn't too busy, is he?
No! He cares for you
and he cares for me,
he isn't too busy, is he? No!

*Continued overleaf*

God always has time for us,
he will always listen.
God always has time for us,
time for ev'ryone.
He cares for you
and he cares for me,
he isn't too busy, is he?
No! He cares for you
and he cares for me,
he isn't too busy for us!



## 71 Paul Crouch and David Mudie

God has a perfect plan for me,
God has a perfect plan for me.
Following Jesus is where I want to be,
God has a perfect plan for me.
He knows the end from the beginning,
he sees the path I need to take.
I have a part to play in God's
amazing plan,
so I will try to follow him each day.

You have a perfect plan for me,
you have a perfect plan for me.
Following you, Lord, is where I want
to be,
you have a perfect plan for me.
You know the end from the beginning,
you see the path I need to take.
I have a part to play in your
amazing plan,
so help me, Lord, to follow you
each day.

God has a perfect plan for you,
God has a perfect plan for you.
To follow Jesus – that's what we want
to do,
God has a perfect plan for you.
God has a perfect plan for me,
God has a perfect plan for me.
Following Jesus is where I want to be,
God has a perfect plan for, his perfect
plan is best for,
God has a perfect plan for me.



## 72 Chris Jackson

God is faithful,
he is the one.
God is faithful,
he's the one
who has called us
to share life with his Son,
Jesus Christ our Lord.



## 73 Capt. Alan Price, CA

*God is good, God is great,*
*he's the one who did create*
*ev'rything that there is by his power.*
*God is good, God is great,*
*he's the one who did create*
*ev'rything that there is by his power.*

Thank you, Lord, for the things I can see,
thank you, thank you, Lord.
Thank you, Lord, for the sounds I can hear,
thank you, thank you, Lord.

Thank you, Lord, for my family,
thank you, thank you, Lord.
Thank you, Lord, for all my friends,
thank you, thank you, Lord.

Thank you, Lord, for the birds in the sky,
thank you, thank you, Lord.
Thank you, Lord, for the ants on the
ground,
thank you, thank you, Lord.

Thank you, Lord, for your love to me,
thank you, thank you, Lord.
Thank you, Lord, that you're always near,
thank you, thank you, Lord.



## 74 Graham Kendrick

God is good, we sing and shout it,
God is good, we celebrate.
God is good, no more we doubt it,
God is good, we know it's true.

And when I think of his love for me,
my heart fills with praise
and I feel like dancing.
For in his heart there is room for me
and I run with arms opened wide.



## 75 Ian Smale

*God is here, God is here,*
*Almighty God is here.*
*Bow down before him*
*in reverence and fear.*
*God is here, God is here,*
*Almighty God is here,*
*Almighty God is here.*

It's hard to imagine how it could ever be
that the maker of the universe is now
here with me.
I'll no longer live in loneliness, nor fear
the enemy.
Almighty God is here.

As I see my generation in sadness and
in pain,
I hear the fools say, 'There's no God',
time and time again.
But fools can never change the fact that
our God is here to reign.
Almighty God is here.

So let's call together all the saints, their
voices to proclaim
that the Father, Son and Spirit will
forever be the same,
and the day will come when every knee
shall bow at Jesus' name.
Almighty God is here.



## 76 Ian Smale

God is here, God is present,
God is moving by his Spirit.
Can you hear what he is saying,
are you willing to respond?
God is here, God is present,
God is moving by his Spirit.
Lord, I open up my life to you,
please do just what you will.
Lord, I won't stop loving you,
you mean more to me than anyone else.
Lord, I won't stop loving you,
you mean more to me than anyone else.



## 77 Alex Simons and Freda Kimmey

God is our Father,
for he has made us his own,
made Jesus our brother,
and hand in hand we'll grow together as
one.
Sing praise to the Lord with the
tambourine,
sing praise to the Lord with clapping
hands.
Sing praise to the Lord with dancing feet,
sing praise to the Lord with our voice.
La, la, la, la, la, etc.

## 78 Unknown

God is so good,
God is so good,
God is so good,
he's so good to me.

He took my sin,
he took my sin,
he took my sin,
he's so good to me.

Now I am free,
now I am free,
now I am free,
he's so good to me.

God is so good,
he took my sin,
now I am free,
he's so good to me.



## 79 Capt. Alan Price, CA

God is the one who wants the best for me,
wants me to be the best that I can be.
Jesus came to show the way that I could know
life in all its fullness if to him I go.
He forgives my sin and fills me ev'ry day
with power to live for Jesus in all I do and say.
There is nothing in my life for which he doesn't care,
he always will be with me, all the time and ev'rywhere.*

* *Last time*
He always will be with me, all the time and ev'rywhere;
he always will be with me, all the time and ev'rywhere.



## 80 Unknown

*God loves you, and I love you,*
*and that's the way it should be.*
*God loves you, and I love you,*
*and that's the way it should be.*

You can be happy, and I can be happy,
and that's the way it should be.
You can be happy, and I can be happy,
and that's the way it should be.

You can be very sad, I can be very sad;
that's not the way it should be.
You can be very sad, I can be very sad;
that's not the way it should be, 'cos . . .

We can love others like sisters and brothers;
and that's the way it should be.
We can love others like sisters and brothers;
and that's the way it should be.



## 81 Derek Llewellyn

God loves you so much,
God wants you so much,
God wants to tell you so much
that he put it in a book for you.

*And it's the Bible.*
*Yes, it's the Bible.*
*Oh, it's the Bible.*
*Yes, he put it in a letter*
*so we could know him better.*

He wants to know you so much,
he wants to know you so much,
God wants to tell you so much
that he put it in a book for,
put it in a book for,
put it in a book for you.

## 82 Michael Forster

*God made a boomerang and called it love,*
*God made a boomerang and called it love,*
*God made a boomerang and called it love,*
*and then he threw it away!*

Love's like a boomerang, that's what we've found,
it comes right back when you throw it around.
Something we can share out,
never seems to wear out,
love's like a boomerang, let's throw it around.

Love's like a boomerang, that's what God planned,
but it's no use if it stays in your hand.
Gotta send it spinning
for a new beginning,
love's like a boomerang, let's throw it around.

Love's like a boomerang, goes with a swing,
now ev'rybody can have a good fling.
Families and nations
join the celebrations,
love's like a boomerang, let's throw it around.



## 83 Capt. Alan Price, CA

*God never gives up,*
*he never gives up,*
*he never gives up on me, no sir!*
*God never gives up,*
*he never gives up,*
*he never will cease to care!*

I know I don't deserve the love
that Jesus has for me.
He died that I could be forgiv'n
and be all I could be!

Even when I forget him
and hardly ever pray,
the Spirit of Jesus deep inside
assures me when I say . . .

Even when I deny him,
pretend that I don't care,
the Spirit of Jesus deep inside
reminds me he's still there!

Even when I might hurt him
with careless words and deeds,
Father God still will love me,
and care for all my needs!
So I'll never give up,
try not to give up,
try not to give up on him, please God!
His Spirit within will help me to win
when I'm tempted to give up on him!



## 84 Iain D. Craig

God's love is deeper than the deepest ocean,
God's love is wider than the widest sea,
God's love is higher than the highest mountain,
deeper, wider, higher is God's love to me.

God's grace is deeper than . . .

God's joy is deeper than . . .

God's peace is deeper than . . .

Deeper, wider, higher,
deeper, wider, higher,
deeper, wider, higher is God to me.

## 85 Unknown

God's not dead, (no), he is alive.
God's not dead, (no), he is alive.
God's not dead, (no), he is alive.
Serve him with my hands,
follow with my feet,
love him in my heart,
know him in my life;
for he's alive in me.



## 86 John Hardwick

God's people aren't super-brave, super-heroes,
they don't have muscles from their heads to their toes.
They're not gladiators, that's easy to see.
In fact, it's amazing, they are just like you and me!
*(Repeat)*
Sometimes scared, shaking and a-shiv'ring.
But let's realise we've got God on our side,
and he can do absolutely anything.
God's people aren't super-brave, super-heroes,
they don't have muscles from their heads to their toes.
They're not gladiators, that's easy to see.
In fact it's amazing, they are just like you and me!



## 87 Jim Bailey

God's rubbered out all my mistakes,
he's erased all my sin.
He's the ruler of creation,
no one measures up to him.
His word gets me straight to the point,
I'm sharp'ner ev'ry day;
I'm reminded of this from the contents
of my pencil case.

*My pencil case, my pencil case;*
*I'm reminded of this from the contents of my pencil case.*
(Repeat)

I am never stationery,
always moving on.
I felt the tip of his love,
now I know that God's right on.
His love's compassed about me,
I'm stapled to his grace;
I'm reminded of this from the contents
of my pencil case.



## 88 Paul Crouch and David Mudie

God trains all his children
as a gardener trains a vine,
watering and pruning
so it grows into the sunshine.
And in time he is rewarded
when he sees fruit on the tree.
So our Father loves to see
the Spirit's fruit in you and me.
Love, joy, peace, patience,
goodness, kindness, faithfulness,
gentleness and self-control.



## 89 Graeme Young

God, you can use me,
God, you can use me,
that the world may hear
the Lord Jesus,
God, you can use me.

. . . that the world may see . . .

. . . that the world may love . . .

God, you can use us . . .
. . . that the world may praise . . .

## 90 Jim Bailey

Go, go, go into the world.
Go, go, go into the world.
Go, go, go into the world.
Tell your mum and dad
the good news that you've had;
Jesus Christ is Lord.

Go, go, go into the world.
Go, go, go into the world.
Go, go, go into the world.
Go and tell the rest
Jesus is the best;
tell every boy and girl.



## 91 Capt. Alan Price, CA

Good or bad, right or wrong,
we have to choose each day.
Truth or lie, share or keep,
ignore the rules or obey.
Jesus is the one we need
to help us choose the right way;
Jesus, you're the one we need,
help us, Lord, today!



## 92 Paul Crouch and David Mudie

Grace is when God gives us
the things we don't deserve.
Grace is when God gives us
the things we don't deserve.
He does it because he loves us,
he does it because he loves us.
Grace is when God gives us
the things we don't deserve.

Mercy is when God does not
give us what we deserve.
Mercy is when God does not
give us what we deserve.
He does it because he loves us,
he does it because he loves us.
Mercy is when God does not
give us what we deserve.



## 93 Doug Horley

*Hands, hands, fingers, thumbs,*
*we can lift to praise you.*
*Hands, hands, fingers, thumbs,*
*we can lift to praise.*
*Hands, hands, fingers, thumbs,*
*we can lift to praise you.*
*Jump front, jump back, yeah!*
*We were made to praise.**

We've got some hands that we
can raise.
We've got a voice to shout your praise,
Jesus!
Got some feet a-made to dance;
let's use them now we've got
the chance.
(Repeat)

* Last time
*We were made to praise you,*
*we were made to praise.*
*We were made to praise you,*
*we were made to praise.*

## 94 Richard Hubbard

Hang on, stand still, stay put, hold tight;
wait for the Spirit of God.
Don't push, don't shove, don't move,
that's right,
just wait for the Spirit of God.
*(Repeat)*

For you will receive the power of God.
You will receive the power of God.
You will receive the power of God
when the Holy Spirit is upon you.

Let go, launch out,
press on, don't fight;
be filled with the Spirit of God.
Move on, make way,
step out, that's right;
be filled with the Spirit of God.
*(Repeat)*

For you have received the power of
God.
You have received the power of God.
You have received the power of God
now the Holy Spirit lives within you.



## 95 Nick Harding

Harvest time is the time when all the
crops are high,
all the food must be cut and stored up
in the dry.
Harvest time – see the fruit, the maize
and wheat,
all the food for us to eat,
it must be harvest time.

Harvest time, we have always got so
much to eat,
but for some just a little is a real feast.
Harvest time – let's remember all the
poor,
and let's try to give them more
after this harvest time.

Harvest time is the time when we should
all thank God
for each grain, ev'ry apple and the green
pea pod.
Harvest time – see the fruit, the maize
and wheat,
so much food for us to eat.
Thank God for harvest time.



## 96 Doug Horley

*Have we made our God too small,
too small?
Have we made our God too small?
He made the heavens and earth
and he reigns on high,
yet he's got the time for you and I.*
(Repeat)

See the glory of God light up the sky,
as the clouds proclaim he reigns on
high.
See the huge expanse of the oceans
wide,
and a billion stars that grace the sky.
I'm awed by the power,
awed by the marks of God all around
me,
yet humbled ev'ry day, by my
unbelieving ways.
I really, really want it to change.

## 97 Mick Gisbey

Have you got an appetite?
Do you eat what is right?
Are you feeding on the word of God?
Are you fat or are you thin?
Are you really full within?
Do you find your strength in him
or are you starving?

*You and me, all should be*
*exercising regularly,*
*standing strong all day long,*
*giving God the glory.*
*Feeding on the living Bread,*
*not eating crumbs but loaves instead;*
*standing stronger, living longer,*
*giving God the glory.*

If it's milk or meat you need,
why not have a slap-up feed,
and stop looking like a weed and start to grow?
Take the full-of-fitness food,
taste and see that God is good,
come on, feed on what you should and be healthy.



## 98 Ralph Chambers

Have you heard about the boy in the multi-coloured coat?
All his brothers thought it was a great big joke,
but he grew up to be Prime Minister you see.
Joseph was on the side of God.

*It's amazing what the Lord can do*
*through a boy or girl like me or you.*
*It cannot be denied that with God on your side,*
*it's amazing what the Lord can do.*

Have you heard about the boy in the lions' den?
Punished by the king for praying to the Lord and then
God's angel came to save his servant from the grave.
Daniel was on the side of God.

Have you heard about the boy with the sling and the stone?
How he fought a ten-foot giant all alone.
God chose him to be king, a most unusual thing.
David was on the side of God.



## 99 Christian Strover

Have you heard the raindrops drumming on the rooftops?
Have you heard the raindrops dripping on the ground?
Have you heard the raindrops splashing in the streams
and running to the rivers all around?

*There's water, water of life,*
*Jesus gives us the water of life;*
*there's water, water of life,*
*Jesus gives us the water of life.*

There's a busy worker digging in the desert,
digging with a spade that flashes in the sun;
soon there will be water rising in the well-shaft,
spilling from the bucket as it comes.

*Continued overleaf*

*There's water, water of life,*
*Jesus gives us the water of life;*
*there's water, water of life,*
*Jesus gives us the water of life.*

Nobody can live who hasn't any water,
when the land is dry, then nothing much grows;
Jesus gives us life if we drink the living water,
sing it so that ev'rybody knows.



## 100 P. A. Taylor

Have you seen the pussy-cat sitting on the wall?
Have you heard his beautiful purr? (purr)
Have you seen the lion stalking round his prey?
Have you heard his terrible roar? (roar)

*One so big, one so small,*
*our heav'nly Father cares for them all;*
*one so big, one so small,*
*our heav'nly Father cares.*

Have you seen the children coming home from school?
Have you heard them shout, 'Hurray!' (Hurray!)
Have you seen the grown-ups coming home from work,
saying, 'What a horrible day!' (What a horrible day!)

*Some so big . . .*



## 101 O. A. Lambert

Heaven is a wonderful place,
filled with glory and grace.
I wanna see my Saviour's face.
Heaven is a wonderful place.
(I wanna go there!)



## 102 Iain Craig

*He is the King of kings and Lord of lords,*
*he is the loving, living Word.*
*He reigns on high and yet he is my friend,*
*and Jesus is his name.*

All my friends at school say I'm a fool
because I trust in him ev'ry day,
and I hold on to what I know is true,
he is the light, the truth, the way.

When I feel far from him, he is still there.
He draws so close as I talk to him in prayer.
He is my Lord and yet he is a King,
and Jesus is his name.



## 103 Kevin Prosch

He is the Lord, and he reigns on high;
he is the Lord.
Spoke into the darkness, created the light.
He is the Lord.
Who is like unto him, never-ending in days;
he is the Lord.
And he comes in power when we call on his name.
He is the Lord.

*Show your power, O Lord our God,*
*show your power, O Lord our God,*
*our God.*

Your gospel, O Lord, is the hope for our nation;
you are the Lord.
It's the power of God for our salvation.
You are the Lord.
We ask not for riches, but look to the cross;
you are the Lord.
And for our inheritance give us the lost.
You are the Lord.

*Send your power, O Lord our God,*
*send your power, O Lord our God,*
*our God.*



## 104 Chris Jackson

*Here I am, Lord,*
*here I am.*
*I'm only a child, Lord,*
*but here I am.*

Make me like Jesus,
fill me with pow'r;
I want to serve you,
that's my desire.



## 105 Merete Åsebøe-Blindheim trans. Capt. Alan Price, CA

*Here I am, ready to go,*
*excitement spreading from head to toe!*
*God has said he's planned a way*
*for me to live my life each day;*
*I could choose a way that's easiest*
*but I know that his way is the best!*

Like a treasure map of old,
the Bible shows the path to follow;
Jesus said, he is the way,
sometimes it's a road that's narrow.
But the Spirit of Jesus is here, deep inside,
a friend always with me, my helper and guide!



## 106 Matt Redman and Capt. Alan Price, CA

Here's a song, bursting out of my heart once again.
Jesus Christ, you're so good that I can't keep it in.
Ev'ry time I think of you, my heart begins to sing . . .

Listen, Lord, to the songs we sing,
la la la, la la la;
they're a sign of the love we bring,
la la la, la la la.

Na na na, na na na . . . (to the tune of 'Here we go' football chant) picking up the song once more at 'Listen, Lord . . .'



## 107 Issac Balinda

*Higher, higher, higher, higher, higher,*
*higher, higher, lift up Jesus higher.*
*Higher, higher, higher, higher, higher,*
*higher, higher, lift up Jesus higher.*

*Lower, lower, lower, lower, lower,*
*lower, lower, lower Satan lower.*
*Lower, lower, lower, lower, lower,*
*lower, lower, lower Satan lower.*

*Continued overleaf*

Cast your burdens on to Jesus,
he cares for you.
Cast your burdens on to Jesus,
he cares for you.

*Higher, higher, higher, higher, higher,*
*higher, higher, lift up Jesus higher.*
*Higher, higher, higher, higher, higher,*
*higher, higher, lift up Jesus higher.*



## 108 Mark and Helen Johnson

*Higher than the highest mountain,*
*deeper than the deepest deep blue sea,*
*stronger than the love of ev'ryone,*
*is the love of Jesus for me!*

We're talkin' 'bout Jesus,
we're talkin' 'bout Jesus,
we're talkin' 'bout Jesus, Jesus,
Jesus and his love for me!

We're singin' 'bout Jesus . . .

We're whisp'rin' 'bout Jesus . . .

We're shoutin' 'bout Jesus . . .



## 109 Unknown

Ho ho ho hosanna,
ha ha halleluia.
He he he he loves me,
and I've got the joy of the Lord.

## 110 Doug Horley

*Hold on to the promises of God,*
*hold on to the promises of God,*
*when it's tough and hard in your back yard*
*you gotta hold on to the promises of God.*

God said to Abraham, 'Hey, you'll have an heir,
get offa the floor, stop laughing like a bear'.
Abraham said, 'But I'm way past my prime,
have you lost count, Lord, 'cause I'm eighty-five'.
God said, 'Well, that's no problem to me,
believe what is said 'cause it's meant to be'. You gotta

Now Abraham believed what God said was true,
but in case he was wrong he had plan number two.
And through his servant he got himself a son.
He thought at last the promise had come,
but God said, 'This is your plan, not mine,
I'll do it my way and in my time'.

God said to Abraham, 'Look up in the sky,
count all the stars way way up high.
That's the size of family I'll give to you,
if you obey what I say in all you do.
That's the good news, but now here's a surprise,
the bad news is, you've gotta be circumcised!'

So Isaac was born and Abram was proud,
but a voice from on high came through clear and loud.
This boy will be a sacrifice.
Abram said, 'Hey, that's not very nice',
but by now he knew it really paid to obey;
he said to Isaac, 'We're going out for the day'.

Tied hand and foot, on his back Isaac lay,
as his Dad raised the knife he knew this was not his day!
But with seconds to spare God stepped in, in time.
Isaac said, 'Phew! Well, you cut that a bit fine!'
God said to Abraham, 'You've passed the last test,
you really have proved you're the best of the best'.



## 111 Carl Tuttle

Hosanna, hosanna, hosanna in the highest!
Hosanna, hosanna, hosanna in the highest!
Lord, we lift up your name,
with hearts full of praise;
be exalted, O Lord, my God!
Hosanna in the highest!

Glory, glory, glory to the King of kings!
Glory, glory, glory to the King of kings!
Lord, we lift up your name,
with hearts full of praise;
be exalted, O Lord, my God!
Glory to the King of kings!



## 112 Hugh Mitchell

How did Moses cross the Red Sea?
How did Moses cross the Red Sea?
How did Moses cross the Red Sea?
How did he get across?
Did he swim? No! No!
Did he row? No! No!
Did he jump? No! No! No! No!
Did he drive? No! No!
Did he fly? No! No!
How did he get across?
God blew with his wind, puff, puff, puff, puff,
he blew just enough, 'nough, 'nough, 'nough, 'nough,
and through the sea he made a path,
that's how he got across.



## 113 Capt. Alan Price, CA

How good of Father God
to give us gifts we don't deserve,
so many ways to demonstrate his power!
It's just because he loves us
and because he wants to use us.
Bring his kingdom to a world that has gone sour.
Holy Spirit we are ready now,
willing now to hear and to obey.
Spirit of Jesus come and touch us now,
give power for your work through us today.

## 114 Graham Kendrick

I am a lighthouse,
a shining and bright house,
out in the waves of a stormy sea.
The oil of the Spirit
keeps my lamp burning;
Jesus, my Lord, is the light in me.
And when people see
the good things that I do,
they'll give praises to God
who has sent us to Jesus.
We'll send out a lifeboat
of love and forgiveness
and give them a hand to get in.
*(Repeat)*
While the storm is raging, whoosh,
whoosh,
and the wind is blowing, oo, oo,
and the waves are crashing,
crash! crash! crash! crash!
I am a lighthouse,
a shining and bright house,
out in the waves of a stormy sea.
The oil of the Spirit
keeps my lamp burning;
Jesus, my Lord, is the light in me.



## 115 Dave Bilbrough

I am a new creation,
no more in condemnation,
here in the grace of God I stand.
My heart is overflowing,
my love just keeps on growing,
here in the grace of God I stand.
And I will praise you, Lord,
yes, I will praise you, Lord,
and I will sing of all that you have done.
A joy that knows no limit,
a lightness in my spirit,
here in the grace of God I stand.



## 116 Capt. Alan Price, CA

*I am a soldier in the army of the Lord,*
*Jesus is my commander,*
*I will listen and obey his ev'ry word,*
*I will not be a bystander.*

I'll fight against the wrong I see,
including ev'ry wrong in me!
I won't let Satan get a hold,
I'll trust in Jesus and be bold!
Na na na na na na na na.

The pow'r of love and the word of the
Lord
is like a mighty two-edged sword.
God's armour I'll put on with glee,
it's his protection over me.
Na na na na na na na na.

Breastplate of righteousness,
belt of truth, shield of faith,
hat of salvation, shoes of the gospel,
sword of the Spirit,
this your armour to put on now.



## 117 Jim Bailey

I am fearfully and wonderfully made.
I am fearfully and wonderfully made.
He who put the stars in place,
and knows them all by name,
has made me fearfully and wonderfully
made.

I am made in the image of God.
I am made in the image of God.
From the top of my head
to the tips of my toes,
my Lord, my name he knows,
I am made in the image of God.

## 118 Capt. Alan Price, CA

*I am part of God's plan,*
*ev'ry one of us can be too,*
*be part of his plan!*

Jesus said his kingdom belongs
to children such as you and me!
I'll live as a child of the King,
be what he wants me to be!

His plan is to win back the world,
make it what it ought to be!
I'll fight as a child of the King,
by the power of his Spirit in me!



## 119 Capt. Alan Price, CA

*I am so glad, I am so very glad*
*that Jesus showed his love for me,*
*makes me the best that I can be!*
*I am so glad, I am so very glad*
*that Jesus is the best friend of all!**

He's always there whatever I do,
working, playing, sleeping too!
There's no place that I can be
where he can never care for me.
Life is such a wonderful thing,
'cos my friend is the King of kings!

* Last time
*that Jesus is the best friend,*
*Jesus is the best friend,*
*Jesus is the best friend of all!*



## 120 Jim Bailey

I am the APPLE of God's eye,
his BANANA over me is love.
He ORANGES his angels to look after me,
as his blessings PLUMmet from above.

Never have to play the GOOSEBERRY,
feel like a LEMON, no not me,
for wherever this MANGOES,
a RASPBERRY it never blows.

*The GREAT FRUIT of God,*
*the GREAT FRUIT of God,*
*the GREAT FRUIT of God*
*it overflows.*
*The GREAT FRUIT of God,*
*the GREAT FRUIT of God,*
*the GREAT FRUIT of God*
*it overflows.*

I will praise him on the TANGERINE,
praise him on the MANDARIN;
SATSUMA or later you will see
there is always a CLEMENTINE for praising him.



## 121 Chris Jackson

| *Boys* | *Girls* |
|---|---|
| I am the way | (I am the way), |
| I am the truth | (I am the truth), |
| I am the life | (I am the life), |

*All:* I am the way, the truth, the life.

| | |
|---|---|
| I am the way | (I am the way), |
| I am the truth | (I am the truth); |

*All:* No one comes to the Father,
no one comes to the Father but by me.

## 122 Marc Nelson

*I believe in Jesus;*
*I believe he is the Son of God.*
*I believe he died and rose again,*
*I believe he paid for us all.*

And I believe he's here now
(I believe that he's here),
standing in our midst;
here with the power to heal now
(with the power to heal),
and the grace to forgive.

*I believe in you, Lord;*
*I believe you are the Son of God.*
*I believe you died and rose again,*
*I believe you paid for us all.*

And I believe you're here now
(I believe that you're here),
standing in our midst;
here with the power to heal now
(with the power to heal),
and the grace to forgive.



## 123 Capt. Alan Price, CA

I can be what God wants me to be,
let the fruit of the Spirit grow in me.
More like Jesus I would be;
Holy Spirit, work in me,
Holy Spirit, work in me.

I can do what God wants me to do,
by the power of the Spirit too,
there are things he's planned for me to
do;
Holy Spirit, work in me,
Holy Spirit, work in me.



## 124 Jim Bailey

*I can do all, (all!) all, (all!) all things*
*through Christ who strengthens me.*
*I can do all, (all!) all, (all!) all things*
*through Christ who strengthens me.*

Go to school: all things.
Obey the rules: all things.
Keep my cool: all things,
through Christ who strengthens me.

Make new friends: all things.
Give and lend: all things.
Make amends: all things,
through Christ who strengthens me.

Pray and sing: all things.
Love our King: all things.
Ev'rything: all things,
through Christ who strengthens me.



## 125 Martin Smith

*Oh, I could sing unending songs*
*of how you saved my soul.*
*Well, I could dance a thousand miles*
*because of your great love.*

My heart is bursting, Lord,
to tell of all you've done.
Of how you changed my life
and wiped away the past.
I wanna shout it out,
from ev'ry roof-top sing.
For now I know that God
is for me, not against me.

Ev'rybody's singing now,
'cos we're so happy!
Ev'rybody's dancing now,
'cos we're so happy!
If only we could see your face
and see you smiling over us
and unseen angels celebrate,
for joy is in this place.



## 126 Mike Burn

*I'd reach for the stars,*
*climb the highest mountain,*
*run a million miles,*
*swim the widest sea,*
*jump over the moon,*
*that's how much I love you,*
*I'd do anything for you, my Lord.*

What can I say? what can I do?
to show you, Jesus, that I love you.
I give you my heart, I give you my song,
O, Jesus, I want you to know . . .

What do you ask? what should I do?
Please help me, Jesus, to follow you.
I give you my life, I give you my will,
O, Jesus, I want you to know . . .



## 127 Mike Burn

If I look in a mirror and there I see my face,
but forget what I look like as soon as I
walk away,
that is what it's like if I hear God's word
and I'm foolish enough not to obey.
'Cos happy are those who hear the word
of God,
happy are those who trust it and obey.
No other way to find true happiness
than to hear the word of God and obey.



## 128 Brian Howard

If I were a butterfly,
I'd thank you, Lord, for giving me
wings,
and if I were a robin in a tree,
I'd thank you, Lord, that I could sing,
and if I were a fish in the sea,
I'd wiggle my tail and I'd giggle with
glee;
but I just thank you, Father, for making
me 'me'.

*For you gave me a heart,*
*and you gave me a smile,*
*you gave me Jesus*
*and you made me your child,*
*and I just thank you, Father,*
*for making me 'me'.*

If I were an elephant,
I'd thank you, Lord, by raising my
trunk,
and if I were a kangaroo,
you know I'd hop right up to you,
and if I were an octopus,
I'd thank you, Lord, for my fine looks;
but I just thank you, Father, for making
me 'me'.

If I were a wiggly worm,
I'd thank you, Lord, that I could squirm,
and if I were a billy goat,
I'd thank you, Lord, for my strong
throat,
and if I were a fuzzy wuzzy bear,
I'd thank you, Lord, for my fuzzy wuzzy
hair;
but I just thank you, Lord, for making
me 'me'.

## 129 Sammy Horner

If Jesus is de vine, we must be de branches.
If Jesus is de vine, we must be de branches.
If Jesus is de vine, we must be de branches,
and bear fruit in the kingdom of God.

If Jesus is de rock, we should be a little bolder.
If Jesus is de rock, we should be a little bolder.
If Jesus is de rock, we should be a little bolder,
to bear fruit in the kingdom of God.

If Jesus is de bread, is your name on the roll now?
If Jesus is de bread, is your name on the roll now?
If Jesus is de bread, is your name on the roll now,
to bear fruit in the kingdom of God?



## 130 Kath Fathers

If we admit to God that we've done wrong
(I'm really sorry, Lord),
he says he will forgive us
and he will keep his promise
and he will make us clean on the inside.
*(Repeat)*
All his promises are true,
let him make them true for you.
All his promises are true,
let him make them true for you.



## 131 Sammy Horner

If you feel unhappy or you're feeling sad,
don't hide your tears, don't hide your tears,
'cause I know of someone who won't treat you bad,
Jesus loves even you.

*Jesus loves even you, friend,*
*Jesus loves even you.*
*He's promised to dry*
*ev'ry tear from your eye,*
*Jesus loves even you.*

If you want to cry when you watch your TV,
don't hold it back, don't hold it back,
for Jesus cries too for those children you see,
Jesus loves even you.

Tonight when you go to your bedroom to sleep,
don't be afraid, don't be afraid,
for Jesus has promised our souls he will keep,
Jesus loves even you.



## 132 Ian White

*If you're going to run the race and win,*
*you've got to know where to begin.*
*You need to learn about the Lord,*
*and start by reading his Word.*

Reading his Word, Genesis and Exodus.
Reading his Word, Leviticus and Numbers.
Reading his Word, Deuteronomy, Joshua and Judges.
Reading his Word, Ruth, Samuel and Kings.

Reading his Word, Chronicles and Ezra.
Reading his Word, Nehemiah and Esther.
Reading his Word, Job, Psalms and
Proverbs.
Reading his Word, Ecclesiastes and Song
of Solomon.

Reading his Word, Isaiah and Jeremiah.
Reading his Word, Lamentations and
Ezekiel.
Reading his Word, Daniel and Hosea.
Reading his Word, Joel and Amos.

Reading his Word, Obadiah and Jonah.
Reading his Word, Micah and Nahum.
Reading his Word, Habakkuk and
Zephaniah.
Reading his Word, Haggai, Zechariah
and Malachi.

Reading his Word, Matthew, Mark, Luke
and John.
Reading his Word, Acts, Romans and
Corinthians.
Reading his Word, Galatians, Ephesians
and Philippians.
Reading his Word, Colossians,
Thessalonians and Timothy.

Reading his Word, Titus and Philemon.
Reading his Word, Hebrews and James.
Reading his Word, the letters of Peter
and John.
Reading his Word, Jude and Revelation.



## 133 Richard Hubbard

If your output exceeds your input,
your upkeep will be your downfall.
But if your input exceeds your output,
you can hold your head up
and push the enemy down.



## 134 Peter and Hanneke Jacobs

If you see a special way
to give the Lord's great love away,
you don't have to wait till you're grown
up,
'cos God can use you now.
If you want to tell someone
the special things that the Lord has
done,
you don't have to wait,
'cos God can use you now!

*God uses kids*
*who open up their hearts to him*
*and let his love flow through them,*
*God uses kids!*
*God uses kids*
*to share his joy in many ways,*
*and as we give his love each day,*
*God uses kids!*

I can pray for God to bring
people that I love to him,
I don't have to wait till I'm grown up,
'cos God can use me now.
I can pray with others who
want to know God's healing too,
I don't have to wait,
'cos God can use me now!



## 135 Mick Gisbey

I have hidden your word in my heart,
that I might not sin against you.
I have hidden your word in my heart,
that I might not sin against you,
that I might not sin against you,
that I might not sin against you.
I have hidden your word in my heart,
that I might not sin against you.

## 136 Paul Field

I just want to thank you, Lord,
for all the things you give,
for all my family and my friends,
for the good life that we live.

Help me learn to look to you,
and care for others more.
Help me trust in you each day,
whenever I'm unsure.

*You will be my guiding light,*
*you will lead me through my life,*
*even in the darkest night,*
*you shine for me.*
*Through my doubts and through my fears,*
*through the laughter and the tears,*
*through the passing of the years,*
*you'll always be my guiding light.*

Lead me always in your steps,
beautiful and true.
Jesus, you will light the way,
and I will follow you.



## 137 Capt. Alan Price, CA

I love the lights on the Christmas trees,
I love the carols we sing,
I love the magic of Christmas time,
but most of all I love Jesus, my King.
We celebrate the birthday of Jesus, God's son,
who left the glory of heaven
and was born a baby in Bethlehem.
A tiny baby like ev'ryone *(first time)*
*(Repeat)*

A human baby like ev'ryone *(second time)*

I love the lights on the Christmas trees,
I love the carols we sing,
I love the magic of Christmas time,
but most of all I love Jesus, my King.



## 138 Mike Burn

I love to be with you, Jesus,
listening to your voice,
and when I hear you speak my name,
my heart and soul rejoice,
and if you said 'jump',
I'd jump for joy,
and if you said 'run',
I'd run to your side,
and if you said 'leap',
I'd take a leap of faith,
and if you said 'dance',
I'd dance for sheer delight.

*To be with you, to be with you,*
*to be with you, oh, it's the best thing.*
*To be with you, to be with you,*
*to be with you, it's the best thing in my life.*



## 139 David Mudie and Paul Crouch

I love you, Lord Jesus,
the King of all things.
You love me, Lord Jesus,
your love never ends.
To you I am special,
your promises are true.
You love me, Lord Jesus,
and Lord, I love you.

## 140 Rob Hayward

I'm accepted, I'm forgiven,
I am fathered by the true and living God.
I'm accepted, no condemnation,
I am loved by the true and living God.
There's no guilt or fear as I draw near
to the Saviour and Creator of the world.
There is joy and peace as I release
my worship to you, O Lord.



## 141 Capt. Alan Price, CA

I'm a full-time Christian,
working for the Lord,
I'm trying to honour Jesus, not seeking a
reward.
Whatever I do, I do for him,
and try my best, you see,
so glory goes to Father God,
and not just to me.

*I'll work for Jesus, whatever I do,*
*I'll work for Jesus, why don't you?*
*I'll work for Jesus, come what may,*
*I'll work for Jesus ev'ry day!*

I'm a full-time Christian,
whatever I may be,
playing, working, or at home,
watching the TV.
I'll make mistakes, I'll get things wrong,
but I will try and see
that glory goes to Father God
and isn't spoilt by me.



## 142 Ron Sivers

*I'm a pow pow pow pow pow pow*
*pow powerpack!*
*I'm a pow pow pow pow pow pow*
*pow powerpack!*

I may be small, but I'm powerful,
God has made me that way,
recharged by the Holy Spirit
ev'ry day.

Being connected to Jesus
lights me on my way,
giving me the power
to live each day.



## 143 Ron Sivers

I'm a winner when I run with Jesus,
I'm a winner when I go his way.
A crown of everlasting joy
will be mine one day.
I'm blessed when I'm faithful to Jesus,
I'm blessed by his promise to me;
because of him I'm heaven-bound,
a winner I will be, a winner you will see,
a winner in Jesus, that's me!



## 144 Ian Smale

I may live in a great big city,
I may live in a village small,
I may live in a tiny house,
I may live in a tower tall,
I may live in the countryside,
I may live by the sea,
but wherever I live, I know
that Jesus also lives with me,
but wherever I live, I know
Jesus lives with me.

## 145 Capt. Alan Price, CA

*I'm enthusiastic, boing, boing, boing!*
*I think it's fantastic, yeah, yeah, yeah!*
*I'm enthusiastic, boing, boing, boing!*
*I think it's fantastic, yeah, yeah, yeah!*

Jesus showed just how much God loves me (you and me!)
That is why I follow him you see,
do you see, do you see, do you see?

I'm gonna work and do what I can do.
Read my Bible, pray and worship too,
yes I will, yes I will, yes I will!



## 146 Jim Bailey

*I'm getting to know God as my Dad,*
*I'm getting to know God as my Father;*
*it's mega, yeah! to know he loves and cares,*
*yes, I'm getting to know I've a Dad upstairs.*

Dads are often busy with important things to do,
but a Father in heaven always has time for you.
Dads are very special but sometimes not around,
but a Father in heaven always can be found.



## 147 Christopher Jackson

I'm gonna be a mighty warrior,
I'm gonna be a mighty warrior,
filled with your Holy Spirit,
filled with power and might.
Oh! mighty warrior,
raising up a banner,
fighting for what's right,
lifting up your name in all the earth.
Though I find it hard, Lord,
I'll try with all my might,
'cos I want to see
your Kingdom come in power.
I'm gonna be a mighty warrior,
I'm gonna be a mighty warrior,
filled with your Holy Spirit,
filled with power and might.
Oh! mighty warrior!
Oh! mighty warrior!



## 148 Doug Horley

*I'm gonna build my house on solid rock,*
*I'm gonna build my house on solid rock,*
*so I don't wake up to a nasty shock,*
*to find nothing but a pile of rubble.*

Don't want to build a house on foundations that will wobble.
Don't want to build a house with any dodgy bricks.
Don't want to build a house that will shake like a jelly.
I want to shout out loud, of this house you can be proud!

Jesus said, 'Take my words and put them into action;
make these words', he said, 'foundations in your life.
Build with care or else your house will surely tumble,
and it's not a clever trick to own a heap of bricks.'

Jesus said, 'Take my words and put them
into action;
make these words', he said, 'foundations
in your life.
And when the river comes and crashes
up against you,
you won't get washed away, instead
you'll cheer and say:

*Yes, I built my house on solid rock,*
*yes, I built my house on solid rock,*
*and I won't wake up to a nasty shock,*
*to find nothing but a pile of rubble.'*



## 149 John Fryer

*I'm gonna clap my hands and shout*
*out loud,*
*I'm gonna raise my voice above the*
*crowd,*
*because Jesus is the one for me.*
*I'm gonna dance and cheer and stamp*
*my feet,*
*I'm gonna sing this song walking*
*down the street,*
*because Jesus is the one for me.*
(Repeat)

J and E and S - U - S;
He's the King and I must say 'Yes!'
Jesus is the one for me!
J and E and S - U - S;
no one else, no second best.
Jesus is the one for me.



## 150 Capt. Alan Price, CA

I'm gonna click, click, click,
I'm gonna clap, clap, clap,
I'm gonna click, I'm gonna clap
and praise the Lord!
Because of all he's done
I'm gonna make him 'number one',
I'm gonna click, I'm gonna clap
and praise the Lord!

I'm gonna zoom, zoom, zoom,
around the room, room, room,
I'm gonna zoom around the room
and praise the Lord!
Because of all he's done,
I'm gonna make him 'number one',
I'm gonna zoom around the room
and praise the Lord!

I'm gonna sing, sing, sing,
I'm gonna shout, shout, shout,
I'm gonna sing, I'm gonna shout
and praise the Lord!
Because of all he's done,
I'm gonna make him 'number one',
I'm gonna sing, I'm gonna shout
and praise the Lord!

I'm gonna click, click, click,
I'm gonna clap, clap, clap,
I'm gonna zoom around the room
and praise the Lord!
Because of all he's done,
I'm gonna make him 'number one',
I'm gonna sing, I'm gonna shout
and praise the Lord!



## 151 Mike Burn

I'm gonna dance on the streets,
I'm gonna sing in the rain,
for the Spirit of God is poured out
again.
I'm gonna shout it aloud,
I'm gonna let the world know
that the river of God has started to flow.

*Continued overleaf*

*And we sing Jesus, Jesus, come!*
*Oh, we will lift your name on high.*
*You are the Son of God, saving one,*
*Jesus, Jesus, come!*



## 152 Capt. Alan Price, CA

*I'm gonna shine, shine, shine,*
*a light in the world I'll be.*
*I want to shine, shine, shine,*
*let people see Jesus in me!*

I want to glorify the Father
by the things I do;
be the person God has made me,
letting his love flow through!

And when it's hard 'n' it's not so easy
to know and do what's right;
I'll trust the Holy Spirit in me,
to help me win each fight.

Even if I fail him often
and my light is dim;
he has promised to forgive me,
I can come back to him!



## 153 Jim Bailey

*I'm gonna walk by faith, not by sight;*
*I'm gonna walk by faith, not by sight.*
*I'm gonna follow Jesus, and do what's right;*
*I'm gonna walk by faith, not by sight.*

Jesus said, 'If you follow me,
you will never live in darkness.'
Jesus said, 'If you follow me,
you will live in the light.'
*(Repeat)*

*I'm gonna watch and pray every day;*
*I'm gonna watch and pray every day.*
*I'm gonna do ev'rything that I heard Jesus say.*
*I'm gonna watch and pray every day.*

Jesus said . . .

*I'm gonna watch and pray . . .*



## 154 Capt. Alan Price, CA

I'm in-right, out-right, up-right,
down-right happy thru' and thru',
I'm in-right, out-right, up-right,
down-right happy 'cos it's true:
Jesus cared for me when he died on Calvary,
I'm in-right, out-right, up-right,
down-right happy thru' and thru'!



## 155 Ian White

I'm just a shepherd, David is my name,
I live in a village called Bethlehem.
My brothers are soldiers
and they're fighting in the war,
but I don't understand what the fighting is for!
I don't understand what the fighting is for!

I go to see my brothers
and I bring them cheese and bread,
I see Goliath and I hear the things he says,
he's big and mean and ugly, he's a very wicked man,
but I'm gonna get him if I can!
I'm gonna get him if I can!

*Well, who's gonna win, tell me,*
*how's it gonna be?*
*Is it gonna be him, or is it gonna be*
*me?*
*I'm not very tall and I'm not very wide,*
*but I've got the fire of the Lord inside!*
*I've got the fire of the Lord inside!*

Well, I don't need spears,
I don't need armour plate,
if the Lord will deliver me, he'll do it
anyway.
I'd rather use something that I know,
I take a little stone and here I go!
I take a little stone and here I go!

Well, Goliath, you can fight me
with your spear and with your sword,
but I come against you in the name of
the Lord!
And ev'ryone who gathers here will
understand
the battle is the Lord's and it's in our
hands,
the battle is the Lord's and it's in our
hands!



## 156 Mike Burn

I'm putting God's armour on,
I'm putting God's armour on,
so I can stand in his might,
fight for what is right
and walk in the light of the Lord.
*(Repeat)*
I put on the breastplate of
righteousness,
put truth around my waist like a belt,
I put on the shoes to announce good
news,
good news of peace in all the earth.
I lift high the shield of faith
to put out the arrows of the enemy,
put salvation on my head like a helmet.
I pick up the sword of the Spirit,
which is the word of the Lord.



## 157 Ian Smale

I'm putting God's gear on and I am
feeling strong,
because I know the Lord is never wrong.
For he has made it clear that he is
always near,
and his perfect love gets rid of fear.
So as I run the race at Jesus' pace,
at the finishing line there'll be no
disgrace.
Lord, I love you, and you love me too,
what a team we make.



## 158 Steve Bradshaw

I'm putting my hand in your hand now,
O Jesus, I ask of you,
let your Spirit flow right through my
heart.
I'm putting my hand in your hand now,
O Jesus, I ask of you,
let your Spirit flow right through my
heart.
Heal me, Lord, touch me, Lord,
let your Spirit flow right through my
heart.
Heal me, Lord, touch me, Lord,
let your Spirit flow right through my
heart.

## 159 Mike Burn

I'm singing your praise, Lord,
I'm singing your praise,
to show the world that I love you, Jesus,
I'm singing your praise.

*So many ways, Lord,*
*so much that I can do*
*to lift your name in all the earth*
*to show that I love you.*

I'm clapping my hands . . .

I'm shouting your name . . .

I'm jumping for joy . . .



## 160 Audrey Traynor

I'm so excited, Lord, I can't keep still;
I've got to jump up and down on my
feet,
'cos when I think about the way that you
love me, Lord,
I know I can't just sit in my seat, no.

*Ooh, it starts in my heart now,*
*then it flows through my body.*
*Ooh, this feeling inside me, I know*
*that it's you.*
*I just can't hide it; got to let it show*
*now, yeah, yeah.*
*Jumping up and down, woa,*
*dancing with Jesus,*
*and I'm spinning round and round,*
*woa,*
*dancing with Jesus now.*
*I clap my hands to show, woa,*
*I love you, Jesus,*
*and I raise my arms to show, woa,*
*I love you, Jesus, now.*

Just being here with you is oh so precious,
it's a feeling I will never forget,
and now I feel your Spirit moving within
me,
Lord, I thank you for this moment we
share, yeah.



## 161 Capt. Alan Price, CA

I'm sorry for the wrong I've done,
I'm sorry for the wrong I've done;
please forgive me, Lord,
please forgive me, Lord,
I'm sorry for the wrong I've done.

I'm sorry for the wrong I've said,
I'm sorry for the wrong I've said;
please forgive me, Lord,
please forgive me, Lord,
I'm sorry for the wrong I've said.

I'm sorry for the wrong I've thought,
I'm sorry for the wrong I've thought;
please forgive me, Lord,
please forgive me, Lord,
I'm sorry for the wrong I've thought.

Thank you for forgiving me,
thank you for forgiving me;
thank you, thank you, Lord,
thank you, thank you, Lord,
thank you for forgiving me!



## 162 Graham Kendrick

I'm special because God has loved me,
for he gave the best thing that he had
to save me;
his own Son, Jesus, crucified to take the
blame,
for all the bad things I have done.

Thank you, Jesus, thank you, Lord,
for loving me so much.
I know I don't deserve anything;
help me feel your love right now
to know deep in my heart
that I'm your special friend.



## 163 Ian Smale

I'm taking on board what God is saying,
I'm taking on board what God is doing,
I'm taking on board what God's
revealing in his word.
I'm taking on board what God is saying,
I'm taking on board what God is doing,
I'm taking on board what God's
revealing by his Spirit.

We're taking on board . . .



## 164 Jim Bailey

I'm working out what it means to follow
Jesus,
adding up what it costs to follow him;
counting the times that his love is
multiplying,
realising he took away my sin.
He's always in my memory,
he'll never cancel what he's done
for me.
When I add it together I calculate
Jesus is great, Jesus is great!



## 165 Richard Hubbard

I'm your child and you are my God.
I thank you, Father, for your loving care.
I'm your child and you are my God.
You've made me special and you're
always there.

I'm your child and you are my God.
I love you, Jesus, you're close to me.
I'm your child and you are my God.
I give you worship, I bow the knee.

I'm your child and you are my God.
Holy Spirit, flow out to me.
I'm your child and you are my God.
You give me power and authority.



## 166 Capt. Alan Price, CA

In all the galaxy there is no one else like
me,
I'm a unique part of Father God's
creation.
Sometimes weak and sometimes strong,
doing right or doing wrong,
God loves this unique part of his
creation.
No matter how I feel about myself,
I'm the object of God's care;
he sent his son that I might know his love
all the time and ev'rywhere!
In all the galaxy there is no one else like
me,
I'm a unique part of Father God's
creation.
Sometimes weak and sometimes strong,
doing right or doing wrong,
God loves this unique part of his
creation.

## 167 Capt. Alan Price, CA

In days of old when knights were bold
and kings ruled the land,
ev'ryone knew just what to do when
they gave a command.
Some kings ruled with kindness, and
others were so mean,
but we have a King named Jesus, the
best there's ever been!
Jesus, the King of kings, he's the King of
love,
Jesus, the King of kings, Lord of heav'n
above,
Jesus, the King of kings, royal majesty,
and his kingdom is in me.



## 168 Sammy Horner

I need faith just to live my life the way I
know I should,
I need faith just to be the way the Lord
says that I could.
I need faith, faith, faith, faith,
faith ev'ry second of my life.

I need faith if I'm gonna hear the words
you say to me,
I need faith if I'm gonna be what you
want me to be.
I need faith, faith, faith, faith,
faith ev'ry second of my life.

I need faith 'cause I really want to see
your kingdom come,
I need faith just to know where all my
strength is coming from.
I need faith, faith, faith, faith,
faith ev'ry second of my life.



## 169 Ian White

In ev'rything that I do, show me what
Jesus would do.
In ev'rything that I do, show me what
Jesus would do.
I will not be afraid, for I can always pray;
show me what Jesus would do.



## 170 Ian Smale

I once was frightened of spiders,
I once was frightened of the dark;
I once was frightened by many, many
things,
especially things that barked.
But now I'm asking Jesus to help these
fears to go,
'cause I don't want them to be part of
me,
no, no, no, no, no.

I once was frightened by thunder,
and frightened of lightning too;
I once was frightened by many, many
things,
that crashed and banged and blew.
But now I'm asking Jesus,
to help these fears to go,
'cause I don't want them to be part
of me,
no, no, no, no, no.



## 171 Judy Bailey

*I reach up high, I touch the ground,*
*I stomp my feet and turn around.*
*I've got to (woo woo) praise the Lord.*
*I jump and dance with all my might,*
*I might look funny but that's all right.*
*I've got to (woo woo) praise the Lord.*

I'll do anything just for my God,
'cos he's done ev'rything for me.
It doesn't matter who is looking on,
Jesus is the person that I want to please.

May my whole life be a song of praise,
to worship God in ev'ry way.
In this song the actions praise his name,
I want my actions ev'ry day to do the same.



## 172 Capt. Alan Price, CA

*Is it spooky, is it weird,*
*that God wants to talk to you and me?*
*Is it something to be feared?*
*No! God wants the best for you and me!*

He speaks through words in the Bible,
through other Christians too;
and shows us the right way we should live,
in what we say and do. Oh,

But through the Holy Spirit,
supernaturally,
he gives us words and pictures,
a gift of prophecy. Oh,

So we should learn to listen
to all that God would say,
and act on what we think he's said,
listen and obey. Oh,



## 173 Capt. Alan Price, CA

Isn't it good to be together,
being with friends old and new?
Isn't it good?
The Bible tells us Jesus, our Lord,
is here too!
Isn't it good to be together,
being with friends old and new?
Isn't it good?
The Bible tells us Jesus, our Lord,
is here too!
He's here! By his Spirit he's with us,
he's here!
His promise is true, he's here!
Though we can't see him, he's here for
me and for you!
He's here! By his Spirit he's with us,
he's here!
His promise is true, he's here!
Though we can't see him, he's here for
me and for you!



## 174 Capt. Alan Price, CA

It's an adventure following Jesus,
it's an adventure learning of him.
It's an adventure living for Jesus,
it's an adventure following him.
Let's go where he leads us,
turn away from wrong;
for we know we can trust him
to help us as we go along.
It's an adventure following Jesus,
it's an adventure learning of him.
It's an adventure living for Jesus,
it's an adventure following him.



## 175 Capt. Alan Price, CA

It's great, great, coming along;
it's great, great, great to belong;
it's great to know we're not wrong;
it's great that Jesus loves us!
It's great, great, great to be here;
it's great, great, knowing he's near;
it's great ev'rybody can hear;
it's great that Jesus loves us!
It's great that Jesus loves us!

## 176 Ian White

*It takes an almighty hand,*
*to make your harvest grow;*
*it takes an almighty hand,*
*however you may sow.*
*It takes an almighty hand,*
*the world around me shows;*
*it takes the almighty hand of God.*

It takes his hand to grow your garden,
all from a secret in a seed;
part of a plan he spoke and started,
and said is 'very good indeed'.

It takes his hand to turn the seasons,
to give the sun and snow their hour;
and in this plan we learn his reason,
his nature and eternal power.

It took his hands to carry sorrow,
for ev'ry sin that we have done;
and on a cross he bought tomorrow,
a world of good, like he'd begun.

And in his hands there is perfection,
that in this land we only taste;
for now, we see a poor reflection,
then, we shall see him face to face.



## 177 Chris Falson

I walk by faith, each step by faith,
to live by faith, I put my trust in you.
*(Repeat)*
Ev'ry step I take is a step of faith;
no weapon formed against me shall
prosper,
and ev'ry prayer I make is a prayer of faith;
and if my God is for me,
then who can be against me?



## 178 Nigel Hemming

*I wanna be a light in the world,*
*I wanna be a light in the world,*
*shining through the darkness so*
*ev'ryone can see.*
*I wanna be a light in the world,*
*I wanna be a light in the world,*
*and nothing, Lord, can ever hide your*
*precious love in me.*

There is no secret in my eyes,
there is no need to run or hide.
I'm not afraid to tell my friends
of your love that never ends.

You take away all my fear,
you fill me with your love.
You give me strength so I can sing,
songs of praise to my King.



## 179 Sammy Horner

I wanna tell you how much I love you.
I wanna tell you how much I care.

Heavenly Father, we are your children,
when we need you, you'll be there.

We wanna tell you how much we love you.
We wanna tell you how much we care.

Heavenly Father, we are your children,
when we need you, you'll be there.



## 180 Doug Horley

I want to be a tree that's bearing fruit,
that God has pruned and caused to
shoot,
Oh, up in the sky, so very, very high.
I want to be, I want to be a blooming tree.

God has promised his Holy Spirit
will water our roots and help us grow.
Listen and obey, and before you know it
your fruit will start to grow, grow, grow,
grow, grow.

You'll be a tree that's bearing fruit,
with a very, very, very strong root,
bright colours like daisies, more fruit
than Sainsbury's,
you'll be a blooming tree.



## 181 Claire Morgans

I want to be like Jesus,
I want to love like Jesus,
I want to listen to his word.
I want to care like he does,
I want to share like he does,
I want to be a child of God.

*Make me more, make me more like Jesus.*
*More, make me more like Jesus.*

I want to be like Jesus,
I want to see like Jesus,
I want to feel the Father's heart.
I want to reach like he does
with love to each like he does,
I want to be a child of God.



## 182 Capt. Alan Price, CA

I want to be salt for Jesus,
salt in the world for him,
spreading the flavour of Jesus,
stirring his goodness in.
I've got the taste of Jesus,
I know what he can do!
I want to be salt for Jesus,
so you can know him too.



## 183 Chris Jackson

I want to worship you all of my life,
give you praise.
I want to serve only you all of my life,
all my days.
For you are a mighty, awesome God,
and you reign in pow'r and you reign in
love.
O Lord, you are God.



## 184 Matt Redman

I will dance, I will sing,
to be mad for my King.
Nothing, Lord, is hindering
the passion in my soul.
*(Repeat)*

And I'll become
even more undignified than this.
I'll become
even more undignified than this.
Na, na, na, na, na, na! Hey!
Na, na, na, na, na, na! Hey!
(Repeat)



## 185 Leona von Brethorst

I will enter his gates with thanksgiving
in my heart,
I will enter his courts with praise,
I will say this is the day that the Lord
has made,
I will rejoice for he has made me glad.
He has made me glad,
he has made me glad,
I will rejoice for he has made me glad.
He has made me glad,
he has made me glad,
I will rejoice for he has made me glad.

## 186 Matt Redman

I will offer up my life
in spirit and truth,
pouring out the oil of love
as my worship to you.
In surrender I must give
my ev'ry part;
Lord, receive the sacrifice
of a broken heart.

*Jesus, what can I give,*
*what can I bring*
*to so faithful a friend,*
*to so loving a King?*
*Saviour, what can be said,*
*what can be sung*
*as a praise of your name*
*for the things you have done?*
*Oh, my words could not tell,*
*not even in part,*
*of the debt of love that is owed*
*by this thankful heart.*

You deserve my ev'ry breath
for you've paid the great cost;
giving up your life to death,
even death on a cross.
You took all my shame away,
there defeated my sin,
opened up the gates of heav'n,
and have beckoned me in.



## 187 Chris Jackson

I will show you my faith by my actions,
I will show you my faith by the things I
do.
I will show you my faith by my actions.
I will glorify you.

I want my life to make a difference,
I want to tell of your great love,
to share my faith with others,
to do what you would do.
Oh, I want to be a help to you, Lord.



## 188 Ian Smale

I will wave my hands
in praise and adoration,
I will wave my hands
in praise and adoration,
I will wave my hands
in praise and adoration,
praise and adoration to the living God.

For he's given me hands
that just love clapping;
one, two, one, two, three,
and he's given me a voice
that just loves shouting
'Hallelujah!'
He's given me feet
that just love dancing;
one, two, one, two, three,
and he's put me in a being
that has no trouble seeing
that whatever I am feeling
he is worthy to be praised.



## 189 Ian Smale

I won't wander off in the darkness,
I don't want to live in the cold.
I'm not going to live like a little sheep,
who's strayed away from the fold.
I'll try and obey the good Shepherd,
as I'm one of his family.
I'm staying close to Jesus
'cos that's the very best place for me to be,
that's the very best place to be.

## 190 Ian Smale

Jehovah Jireh, God will provide,
Jehovah Rophe, God heals;
Jehovah M'keddesh, God who sanctifies,
Jehovah Nissi, God is my banner.

Jehovah Rohi, God my shepherd,
Jehovah Shalom, God is peace;
Jehovah Tsidkenu, God our
righteousness,
Jehovah Shammah, God who is there.



## 191 Capt. Alan Price, CA

Jesus came proclaiming God's kingdom
was at hand,
for all who would believe in him,
obeying his command;
and now he sends his deputies like you
and me today,
to share God's love in ev'rything we do
and what we say.

*I've got my badge inside,*
*I'm a deputy for Jesus,*
*by the Holy Spirit I am marked and*
*kept for God.*
*I'll wear my badge with pride,*
*I'm a deputy for Jesus,*
*under his authority to live and work*
*for God!*

Set captives free from Satan's grip, pray
for the sick as well,
wherever you may find yourself, the
Good News you must tell!
As Jesus sent disciples then, he sends
us out today,
as deputies for Jesus we'll follow and
obey.



## 192 Matt Redman

Jesus Christ, I think upon your sacrifice;
you became nothing, poured out to
death.
Many times I've wondered at your gift of
life,
and I'm in that place once again,
I'm in that place once again.

*And once again I look upon*
*the cross where you died.*
*I'm humbled by your mercy*
*and I'm broken inside.*
*Once again I thank you,*
*once again I pour out my life.*

Now you are exalted to the highest
place,
King of the heavens, where one day I'll
bow.
But for now I marvel at this saving
grace,
and I'm full of praise once again,
I'm full of praise once again.

Thank you for the cross, thank you for
the cross,
thank you for the cross, my friend.
Thank you for the cross, thank you for
the cross,
thank you for the cross, my friend.



## 193 Steve Israel and Gerrit Gustafson

*Jesus Christ is the Lord of all,*
*Lord of all the earth.*
*Jesus Christ is the Lord of all,*
*Lord of all the earth.*
(Repeat)

*Continued overleaf*

Only one God,
over the nations,
only one Lord of all;
in no other name
is there salvation,
Jesus is Lord of all.

*Jesus Christ is the Lord of all,*
*Lord of all the earth.*
*Jesus Christ is the Lord of all,*
*Lord of all the earth.*

Jesus Christ is Lord of all,
Jesus Christ is Lord of all.
Jesus Christ is Lord of all,
Jesus Christ is Lord of all.



## 194 Margaret Cropper, adapt. Stephen Hopkinson

Jesus' hands were kind hands doing good to all,
healing pain and sickness, blessing children small,
and my hands should serve him, ready at his call.
Jesus' hands were kind hands doing good to all.



## 195 Paul Mazak

Jesus is a friend of mine, praise him.
Jesus is a friend of mine, praise him.
Praise him, praise him.
Jesus is a friend of mine, praise him.

Jesus died to set us free, praise him . . .

He gave us the victory, praise him . . .

Jesus is the King of kings, praise him . . .



## 196 Gill Hutchinson

Jesus is greater than the greatest heroes,
Jesus is closer than the closest friends.
He came from heaven and he died to save us,
to show us love that never ends.
*(Repeat)*

Son of God, and the Lord of glory,
he's the light, follow in his way.
He's the truth, that we can believe in,
and he's the life, he's living today.
*(Repeat)*



## 197 Julia Plaut

Jesus is my friend and I'm a friend of Jesus.
Jesus is my friend and I'm a friend of his.
I can talk to him any time I like.
He's always listening,
that's how I know that Jesus is my friend
and I'm a friend of his.



## 198 Capt. Alan Price, CA

*Jesus isn't dead any more,*
*that is why we sing.*
*Jesus isn't dead any more,*
*he's alive and he's the King of heaven.*

Killed on a cross and sealed in a tomb,
but that was not the end;
God brought Jesus back to life,
now he's our living friend.

He went back to be with God,
but we know he's still near;
Jesus sent the Spirit of God,
and he is always here with us.

*Jesus isn't dead any more,*
*that is why we sing;*
*Jesus isn't dead any more,*
*he's alive, and he's our King.*



Here in my weakness, his strength is so clear,
thank you, Lord Jesus, you're mighty, yet here.
I praise you for taking all of my fear.
Help me to trust you and know you are near;
help me to trust you and know you are near.



## 199 Sammy Horner

Jesus is our shepherd, we must be his sheep,
he said that he'd protect us and give us food to eat,
and if a wolf comes close to us
a shepherd makes him flee,
I don't mind being in his flock, it doesn't sound baa'd to me.
It doesn't sound baa'd to me.
It doesn't sound baa'd to me.
Well, I don't mind being in his flock,
it doesn't sound baa'd to me.



## 200 Sarah Clark

Jesus is special, special to me,
he gave his life so I could be free.
He is my friend who never leaves me.
He is so special, special to me;
he is so special, special to me.

Jesus forgave me for all of my wrong,
came to the earth so we could belong
in his kingdom, close to his heart,
Making me special, he set me apart;
making me special, he set me apart.

## 201 Capt. Alan Price, CA

Jesus is the lighthouse, shining all around,
shining in the darkness, where evil things abound.
Jesus is the lighthouse, showing us the way,
we can leave the darkness, live the Jesus way.

Jesus is the foghorn when trouble's very near,
when hidden dangers threaten, his warning sound you hear.
Jesus is the lighthouse, showing us the way,
we can miss the dangers, live the Jesus way.

Shine your light in me, Lord, I want to live for you,
help me shine for you, Lord, in all I say and do.
I want to be a lighthouse for Jesus ev'ry day,
help me make a difference in your world, I pray!

## 202 Paul Field

Jesus is the password, pass it on.
Jesus is the password, pass it on.
Don't keep it a secret, pass the news along.
Jesus is the password, pass it on.
Pass it on, pass it on, until everybody knows.
Pass it on, pass it on, that's the way the kingdom grows.
Pass it on, pass it on, until all the world has heard.
Pass it on, pass it on, that Jesus is Lord.



## 203 Roger Jones

*Jesus, I will come with you, I will follow in your way.*
*I will trust you, I will bring you all I have today.*
*Jesus, you're the way, Jesus, you're the truth,*
*Jesus, you're the life, praise your name!*

Amazing grace, how sweet the sound,
that could save a wretch like me.
I once was lost but now I'm found,
was blind but now I see.

Gentle Jesus, meek and mild,
look upon a little child.
Pity my simplicity,
loving him who first loved me.

Let us with a gladsome mind,
praise the Lord for he is kind.
For his mercies aye endure,
ever faithful, ever sure.

Praise God from whom all blessings flow,
praise him all creatures here below.
Praise him above ye heav'nly host,
praise Father, Son and Holy Ghost.



## 204 Philip Hawthorne

Jesus, Jesus, here I am;
Jesus, Jesus, take my hand.
You give to ev'ryone a love that won't end.
Thank you, Jesus, you're my friend.



## 205 Leon and Sheryl Olguin

Jesus, Jesus, I love you, I love you.
Jesus, Jesus, I love you, I love you.

Jesus, Jesus, I adore you, I adore you.
Jesus, Jesus, I adore you, I adore you.

You are lovely;
my eyes long to see your face,
and see the scars you bore for me.

Jesus, Jesus, I love you, I love you.
Jesus, Jesus, I love you, I love you,
I love you, I love you, I love you, I love you.

## 206 Sue Howson

*Jesus, life giver.*
*Jesus, my Saviour.*
*Jesus, Jesus, Jesus.*

You shed your blood
on Calvary.
You gave your life for me.

I come to you
to bow my knee.
You are my Lord and King.



## 207 Graham Kendrick

Jesus' love has got under our skin,
Jesus' love has got under our skin.
Deeper than colour oh;
richer than culture oh;
stronger than emotion oh;
wider than the ocean oh.
Don't you want to celebrate
and congratulate somebody,
talk about a family!
It's under our skin, under our skin.

| | |
|---|---|
| *Leader* | Ev'rybody say love: |
| *All* | love. |
| *Leader* | Ev'rybody say love: |
| *All* | love, |
| *Leader* | love, |
| *All* | love. |

Isn't it good to be
living in harmony.
Jesus in you and me;
he's under our skin,
under our skin,
he's under our skin,
under our skin.



## 208 H. W. Rattle

Jesus' love is very wonderful,
Jesus' love is very wonderful,
Jesus' love is very wonderful,
oh, wonderful love!
So high you can't get over it,
so low you can't get under it,
so wide you can't get round it,
oh, wonderful love!



## 209 Graham Kendrick

Jesus put this song into our hearts,
Jesus put this song into our hearts,
it's a song of joy no one can take
away,
Jesus put this song into our hearts.

Jesus taught us how to live in
harmony,
Jesus taught us how to live in
harmony,
different faces, different races, he made
us one,
Jesus taught us how to live in
harmony.

Jesus taught us how to be a family,
Jesus taught us how to be a family,
loving one another with the love that
he gives,
Jesus taught us how to be a family.

Jesus turned our sorrow into dancing,
Jesus turned our sorrow into dancing,
changed our tears of sadness into rivers
of joy,
Jesus turned our sorrow into a dance.

## 210 Chris Jackson

Jesus, reign in me,
Jesus, reign in me;
take your place within my heart
and, Jesus, reign in me.

Jesus, you're my King,
Jesus, you're my King;
take your place within my heart
and, Jesus, you're my King.

Jesus, live in me,
Jesus, live in me;
take your place within my heart
and, Jesus, live in me.

Jesus, forgive me,
Jesus, forgive me;
take your place within my heart
and, Jesus, forgive me.

Jesus, I love you,
Jesus, I love you;
take your place within my heart
and, Jesus, I love you.



## 211 Sue Howson

Jesus, rock of my salvation,
Jesus, lover of my soul;
you alone give life that lasts for ever,
you alone can make me whole.
Call me up; call me higher.
Turn me towards you once again.
As the fragrance of your holiness
lingers in my heart,
I put my trust in you, my Lord and friend.

On this rock I will build my life.
On this rock I've found a love that satisfies.
On this rock I will live and never die.
On this rock I will build my life.



## 212 Roger Jones

*Jesus rode a donkey into town.*
*Many folks turned out from miles around.*
*What a sight to see,*
*a man to set men free,*
*riding on a donkey into town.*

Jesus, is it true, the things the people say of you?
Did you really make a blind man see?
And if all I've heard about you turns out to be true,
can you really do the same for me?

Tell me, do you think he'll take the Roman guards by storm?
Do you think he'll show the priests the door?
Wonder if he's pleased by all the shouting from the crowd,
even by the palms upon the floor.

Hosanna, hosanna,
blessed is the man,
that cometh in the name,
cometh in the name of the Lord!
*(Repeat)*



## 213 Derek Llewellyn

Jesus, send me the helper,
send me the helper to help me.
Jesus, send me the Holy Spirit,
send the Holy Spirit to me.

He gives us love to keep on loving.
He makes us brave to do what is right.
He gives us faith to keep on going.
He gives us power to keep us shining so bright.

## 214 Mike Burn

Jesus, thank you for the cross,
holding nothing back,
you did all your Father asked.
I'll never know just how it felt
as you died, lifted high.
I know it hurt, I know the pain
was more than words could ever say.
You had a choice,
you chose to die,
your sacrifice has saved my life,
what can I say?
Oh, Jesus, you gave your life for me,
so precious the blood you shed.
You made a way to heaven
by dying in my place.
Jesus, thank you for the cross.



## 215 Capt. Alan Price, CA

Jesus, touch me now,
please, I ask you, now.
Do your healing work in me,
your Spirit working tenderly,
make me the best that I can be,
O, Jesus, touch me now,
O, Jesus, touch me now.

Jesus, use me now,
please, I ask you, now.
Do your healing work through me,
your power working lovingly,
a useful servant I would be,
O, Jesus, use me now,
O, Jesus, use me now.



## 216 Capt. Alan Price, CA

*Jesus wants me,*
*Jesus wants me,**
*Jesus wants me to follow him.*

Jesus called to fishermen, said,
'Come, follow me!
Speak and heal with my power
and my authority.'

Jesus still calls his people,
there's a job to be done;
no matter who you are
there's a role for ev'ryone.

There's a cost to following,
of that we may be sure;
but we'll get back ev'rything we give
and even more.

* Last time
*Jesus help us to follow you!*



## 217 John Gibson

*Jesus, we celebrate your victory;*
*Jesus, we revel in your love.*
*Jesus, we rejoice you've set us free;*
*Jesus, your death has brought us life.*

It was for freedom that Christ has set us
free,
no longer to be subject to a yoke of
slavery;
so we're rejoicing in God's victory,
our hearts responding to his love.

His Spirit in us releases us from fear,
the way to him is open, with boldness
we draw near.
And in his presence our problems
disappear;
our hearts responding to his love.

## 218 Capt. Alan Price, CA

Jesus, we thank you;
Lord, you are here.
Thank you for loving us,
as we draw near.



## 219 Capt. Alan Price, CA

*Jesus, you are here.*
*(Jesus you are here.)*
*Jesus, we know you're near.*
*(Jesus we know you.)*

As a sign of worship
we lift our hands in praise,
because you've shown your love to us
in many different ways,
and we worship you, our Lord.

In our songs of worship
we lift our voice to you,
accept the love and thanks we bring
for all the things you do,
and we worship you, our Lord.

I lift my head up to you
in expectancy,
ready to receive your love,
your gift of grace to me,
and I worship you, my Lord.



## 220 Pete Simpson

Jesus, you are my King,
blessed Redeemer,
blessed Redeemer,
Jesus, you are my King,
blessed Redeemer.

Jesus, you are my Lord,
beautiful Saviour,
beautiful Saviour,
Jesus, you are my Lord,
beautiful Saviour.

Jesus, you are my rock,
King of the nations,
King of the nations,
Jesus, you are my rock,
King of the nations.



## 221 Bev Gammon

Jesus, you gave ev'rything for me,
and I want to learn to give to you
through the way I use my time,
my money and my talents;
help me give them all to please you.



## 222 Paul Crouch and David Mudie

*Jesus, you're the King.*
*Lord of ev'rything.*
*You are God's son,*
*you're number one,*
*and that is why we sing.*
(Repeat)

Jesus, you came down from heav'n
to the earth to serve us.
You died but then you rose again.
Glory, halleluia!

Help me to be more like you;
ev'ry day I need you.
I want to praise your name right now.
Here we go again!

## 223 Capt. Alan Price, CA

Just as the Father sent you, Lord,
with pow'r and authority;
just as the Father sent you, Lord,
so you are sending me.
I'm willing to be used, Lord,
in any way you choose,
I'll try not to be too busy
when it's me you want to use.
Just as the Father sent you, Lord,
with pow'r and authority;
just as the Father sent you, Lord,
I want you to send me.



## 224 Capt. Alan Price, CA

*Keep me close to you*
*in ev'rything I do today,*
*Jesus, help me to be careful*
*in ev'ry way*. Mm.*

If I watch things that are bad for me,
things of which you'd disapprove,
help me to turn my eyes away,
or even get up and move.

When others use bad or dirty words,
help me to know what to do.
Stop me if ever I'm tempted
to do the same thing too.

If ever I get in bad places
with those who would cause me to stray,
Lord, let your light shine out from me,
or help me to get right away.

* Last time
*In all that I see and I say,*
*in all that I hear and do,*
*keep me, Lord, close to you. Mm.*



## 225 Mark and Helen Johnson

Let me tell you about a baby,
and his family.
It is written down in the Bible
so you might believe.
Many men had told of his coming,
down through history.
Now the time had come
for fulfilment of their prophecy.

*And they called his name Jesus,*
*Jesus the Saviour.*
*And they called his name Jesus,*
*Son of the most high God.*
(Repeat)

There was once a young girl called Mary,
only in her teens.
She was visited by an angel,
sent to Galilee.
And he told her she'd have a baby,
how she couldn't see.
Yet it was her will to obey him,
so it was agreed.

Well, in those days Caesar Augustus
issued a decree,
and so Mary went with her husband
where they had to be.
There was nowhere else but a stable,
where they both could sleep.
It was there that she had her baby,
born for you and me.



## 226 Jim Aldwinckle and Ron Sivers

Let's celebrate and clap our hands,
let's sing for joy and dance around;
let's raise our hands and praise his name,
for Jesus is our King.
Alleluia.

## 227 Kath Fathers

*Let's get fit,*
*let's get fit,*
*let's get fit,*
*let's get fit.*

It's time for the body to grow now,
it's time for the fruit to show now,
it's time for the world to know now,
so let's get fit.
It's time for the Church to fight now,
it's time to release the light now,
let's train with all our might now,
and let's get fit.

For those who worship the Lord,
the Son of righteousness will rise
with healing in his wings.
For those who worship the Lord,
the Son of righteousness will rise
with healing in his wings.
And you will break out and jump like calves from the stall
(break out and jump like calves from the stall),
break out and skip like calves from the stall
(break out and skip).

*Let's get fit . . .*

It's time to increase the pace now,
it's time for us all to race now,
let's step into his grace now,
and let's get fit.
Let all creation sing now,
he's giving us a time of spring now,
it's time for us all to win now,
so let's get fit.



## 228 Yvonne Scott

Let's sing and make music to the Lord.
Let's sing and make music to the Lord.
Give thanks to God the Father,
give thanks to Jesus his Son.
Give thanks to God the Father,
give thanks to Jesus his Son.

Let's praise and make music to the Lord.
Let's praise and make music to the Lord.
Give thanks to God the Father,
give thanks to Jesus his Son.
Give thanks to God the Father,
give thanks to Jesus his Son.



## 229 Chris Jackson

Let us run with determination,
the race that lies before us;
let us keep our eyes fixed on Jesus.
Let us run with determination,
the race that lies before us;
let us keep our eyes fixed on Jesus.



## 230 Capt. Alan Price, CA

Let us sing and praise God for all that he has done,
for loving us so much in sending his Son.
Let us sing and let him know, let our praises overflow,
let us sing, let us shout, hallelujah!

Let us sing and praise God, let him
know just how we feel,
by our words and actions, show our love
for him is real.
Let us laugh, take a chance, lift our feet
and have a dance,
as we sing, as we shout, hallelujah!

Let us pray to the Lord that we'll never
let him down,
never let temptation cause our
friendship to break down.
Holy Spirit come right in and keep us
close to him,
always sing, always shout, hallelujah!



## 231 Paul Field

Let your love shine through these eyes
of mine,
let me be a light for you each day.
Let your love show to ev'ryone I know,
help me learn to follow in your way.

*Hand in hand for ever,*
*never let me go,*
*sure enough together,*
*wherever I may go.*
*No matter where life leads,*
*give me faith to see your plan,*
*so ev'ry step I take,*
*I take with you hand in hand.*

Jesus, you are my bright shining star,
your word and your Spirit lead me on.
The best I can do, is a life shared with
you,
only in your love can I be strong.



## 232 Capt. Alan Price, CA

*Life is like a big wide ocean*
*and we're sailing the ocean with Jesus*
*our friend.*
*The journey is long and the weather*
*uncertain,*
*but Jesus is with us from beginning*
*to end.*

Jesus knows the best course to sail.
Let's ask him to guide us.
Jesus knows the best course to sail,
with the Holy Spirit compass inside us!
Wa! Wa! Wa! Wa!



## 233 Doug Horley

*Lift his name high,*
*let the world know*
*that the God of creation is alive*
*and well.*
*Lift his name high,*
*let the world know*
*that the way to salvation,*
*the hope for our nation,*
*is Jesus, and he is alive.*

Jesus is the King of glory,
this is no fairy story,
let the world know Jesus is alive.
Mending lives, hurt and broken,
words of healing spoken,
let the world know Jesus is alive.



## 234 Rick Founds

Lord, I lift your name on high;
Lord, I love to sing your praises.
I'm so glad you're in my life;
I'm so glad you came to save us.
*(Repeat)*

*Continued overleaf*

*You came from heaven to earth*
*to show the way,*
*from the earth to the cross,*
*my debt to pay;*
*from the cross to the grave,*
*from the grave to the sky,*
*Lord, I lift your name on high.*



## 235 Iain Craig

Lord, I want to be in your family,
Lord, I want to know I belong.
Lord, I want to be in your family,
I know that faith in you will make me strong.

*I don't want to be the one*
*who says you're not for me,*
*I don't want to be left outside,*
*so, o, o, o, o, o,*
*Lord, I want to be in your family*
*where I can feel so safe and warm.*

Now I know there might be times that I will let you down,
the things I say might not bless your name.
But Lord, I know you'll never let me go,
yesterday, today, for ever, you're the same.



## 236 Chris Jackson

Lord, look into my heart,
tell me what you see within me.
Lord, let your fire burn,
burn away the sin within me.
'Cos I want to know,
I want to know,
I want to put things right.
For I want to be,
I want to be holy in your sight.
Lord, look into my heart,
tell me what you see within me.



## 237 Graham Kendrick

Lord, the light of your love is shining,
in the midst of the darkness, shining;
Jesus, Light of the World, shine upon us,
set us free by the truth you now bring us.
Shine on me, shine on me.

*Shine, Jesus, shine,*
*fill this land with the Father's glory;*
*blaze, Spirit, blaze,*
*set our hearts on fire.*
*Flow, river, flow,*
*flood the nations with grace and mercy;*
*send forth your word, Lord,*
*and let there be light.*

Lord, I come to your awesome presence,
from the shadows into your radiance;
by the blood I may enter your brightness,
search me, try me, consume all my darkness.
Shine on me, shine on me.

As we gaze on your kingly brightness,
so our faces display your likeness,
ever changing from glory to glory;
mirrored here may our lives tell your story.
Shine on me, shine on me.

## 238 Ken McGreavy and Wes Sutton

Lord, we cry out to you.
Lord, we cry out to you.
Have mercy,
have mercy on us.

Open our eyes to see.
open our eyes to see.
We want to see,
we want to see you.

Lord we will follow you.
Lord we will follow you.
We'll follow you,
we'll follow in the way of truth.



## 239 Mick Ray

Lord, we give you praise;
our prayer of thanks to you we bring.
We sing our songs to you,
for praise belongs to you.
Lord, we give you praise.

Your love goes on and on;
you never change, you never turn.
Our hands we raise to you,
and bring our praise to you;
Lord, we give you praise.



## 240 Judy Bailey

Lord, we lift you high
when we praise your name,
when we worship you
and our hands are raised,
that is how we lift you up.
Lord, we lift you high
when we tell the truth,
when we give our best
in ev'rything we do,
that is how we lift you up.

*By our voices be lifted, lifted,*
*by our actions, Lord, be lifted high.*
*By our love, Lord, be lifted, lifted,*
*by our lives, O Lord, be lifted high.*

Lord, we lift you high
when we're good and kind;
when we turn from wrong
and we do what's right,
that is how we lift you up.
Lord, we lift you high
when we shine like stars;
when we tell our friends
just how good you are,
that is how we lift you up.

You are God, Jesus the Lord of all,
we place you above all else.
So shine through me
and keep drawing the world to your
heart.



## 241 Ian Smale

Lord, we've come to worship you,
Lord, we've come to praise;
Lord, we've come to worship you
in oh so many ways.
Some of us shout and some of us
sing,
and some of us whisper the praise we
bring;
but, Lord, we all are gathering
to give you our praise.

## 242 Ian Smale

Lord, you gave me joy in my heart,
joy in my heart always,
and it's you I want to praise.

Lord, you gave me peace in my mind,
peace in my mind always;
peace in my mind, joy in my heart,
and it's you I want to praise.

Lord, you gave me a song in my mouth,
a song in my mouth always;
a song in my mouth, peace in my mind,
joy in my heart,
and it's you I want to praise.

Lord, you gave me hands that will clap,
hands that will clap always;
hands that will clap, a song in my
mouth,
peace in my mind, joy in my heart,
and it's you I want to praise.

Lord, you gave me feet that can dance,
feet that can dance always;
feet that can dance, hands that will
clap,
a song in my mouth, peace in my mind,
joy in my heart,
and it's you I want to praise.

Lord, you gave me a love for others,
a love for others always;
a love for others, feet that can dance,
hands that will clap, a song in my
mouth,
peace in my mind, joy in my heart,
and it's you I want to praise.



## 243 Ian Smale

Lord, you put a tongue in my mouth
and I want to sing to you.
Lord, you put a tongue in my mouth
and I want to sing to you.
Lord, you put a tongue in my mouth
and I want to sing only to you.
Lord Jesus, free us in our praise;
Lord Jesus, free us in our praise.

Lord, you put some hands on my arms
which I want to raise to you . . .

Lord, you put some feet on my legs
and I want to dance to you . . .



## 244 Capt. Alan Price, CA

*Lord, you've promised through your*
*Son,*
*you'll forgive the wrongs we've done;*
*we confess them, ev'ry one,*
*please, dear Lord, forgive us.*

Things we've done and things we've said,
we regret the hurt they spread.
Lord, we're sorry.
Lord, we're sorry.

Sinful and unkind thoughts too,
all of these are known to you.
Lord, we're sorry.
Lord, we're sorry.

And the things we've left undone,
words and deeds we should have done.
Lord, we're sorry.
Lord, we're sorry.

*Last refrain:*
*Lord, you've promised, through your Son,*
*you'll forgive the wrong we've done;*
*we receive your pardon,*
*Lord, as you forgive us.*



## 245 Derek Rowlinson

Love, love your enemies,
do good to those who hate you;
love, love your enemies,
do good to those who hate you.
Forgive others and God will forgive you,
give to others and God will give back;
forgive others and God will forgive you,
give to others and God will give back to you.



## 246 Jack W. Hayford

Majesty, worship his majesty,
unto Jesus be glory, honour and praise.
Majesty, kingdom authority
flows from his throne unto his own,
his anthem raise.
So exalt, lift up on high the name of Jesus;
magnify, come glorify Christ Jesus the King.
Majesty, worship his majesty,
Jesus who died, now glorified,
King of all kings.



## 247 Jimmy and Carol Owens

Make a joyful noise unto the Lord, all the earth,
make a joyful noise unto the Lord.
Make a joyful noise unto the Lord, all the earth,
make a joyful noise unto the Lord.
Make a loud noise (NOISE) and rejoice, sing praises,
make a joyful noise unto the Lord.
Make a loud noise (NOISE) and rejoice, sing praises,
make a joyful noise unto the Lord.

*Where it says (NOISE) make a quick sound – clap, whistle, shout, etc.*



## 248 Sebastian Temple

Make me a channel of your peace.
Where there is hatred, let me bring your love.
Where there is injury, your pardon, Lord,
and where there's doubt, true faith in you.

*O Master, grant that I may never seek*
*so much to be consoled as to console,*
*to be understood, as to understand,*
*to be loved, as to love with all my soul.*

Make me a channel of your peace.
Where there's despair in life, let me bring hope.
Where there is darkness, only light,
and where there's sadness, ever joy.

Make me a channel of your peace.
It is in pardoning that we are pardoned,
in giving of ourselves that we receive,
and in dying that we're born to eternal life.

## 249 Graham Kendrick

Make way, make way, for Christ the King
in splendour arrives;
fling wide the gates and welcome him
into your lives.

*Make way (make way),*
*make way (make way),*
*for the King of kings*
*(for the King of kings);*
*make way (make way),*
*make way (make way),*
*and let his kingdom in!*

He comes the broken hearts to heal,
the pris'ners to free;
the deaf shall hear, the lame shall dance,
the blind shall see.

And those who mourn with heavy hearts,
who weep and sigh,
with laughter, joy and royal crown
he'll beautify.

We call you now to worship him
as Lord of all,
to have no gods before him,
their thrones must fall.



## 250 David Ruis

Mercy is falling, is falling, is falling,
mercy it falls like the sweet spring rain.
Mercy is falling, is falling all over me.
*(Repeat)*

Hey O, I receive your mercy.
Hey O, I receive your grace.
Hey O, I will dance for evermore.
*(Repeat)*



## 251 Mark and Helen Johnson

Midnight, there's the strangest feeling in the air tonight;
there's something going on but I can't make it out,
I wonder what it's all about?
Starlight, breaking through the darkness in the dead of night,
illuminates the path that takes you out of sight,
and all the way to Bethlehem.

*Tonight's events were planned in heaven,*
*the greatest story ever penned.*
*Heaven and earth have come together,*
*and life has come to Bethlehem.*

Angels – taking care of things that only they can do,
are waiting in the wings to bring the joyful news,
it's going to turn the world around.
Strangers – having made arrangements for a night or two,
have found accommodation in the crowded rooms.
The house is packed in Bethlehem.

Shepherds – minding their own business looking after things,
are startled by an unexpected happening,
as angel choirs appear to them.
Wise men – taking charts and telescopes and compasses,
investigate the star that takes them travelling,
until they come to Bethlehem.

## 252 Robyn Barnett

*Mind the gap! (I tell you).*
*Mind the gap! (don't fall down).*
*Mind the gap! (I heard him say).*
*You need to get across (but how?).*
*You need to get across (just look!).*
*You need to get across over the bridge.*

Long ago when the world began,
we and God were best of friends,
walked and talked together all day long,
he never wanted this to end.
Then we let go of his strong hand,
chose to turn and walk away,
made a gap so deep and wide –
was this how we'd have to stay?

Think of things that we all do and say,
when we're selfish and unkind.
Broken objects we can stick and mend,
but not our broken hearts and lives.
Don't give up or feel despair,
whether girl or boy, woman or man.
God's the best friend we could have;
here's the story of his rescue plan.

It was just two thousand years ago,
Jesus Christ was born on earth;
he was so amazing, time was changed,
it began again from Jesus' birth!
He said, 'Look! I am the bridge!'
and the price he paid for wood and nails
was his life, but the price was right,
for the Cross shows love that never fails.



## 253 Julia Plaut

Mister Cow, how do you say to the Lord, 'I love you?'
Mister Cow, how do you say to the Lord, 'I love you?'
'Well I stand around in the field all day,
and it gives me plenty of time to say:
Moo! Moo! Moo!'

Mister Sheep, how do you say to the Lord, 'I love you?'
Mister Sheep, how do you say to the Lord, 'I love you?'
'Well I stand around in the field all day,
and it gives me plenty of time to say:
Baa! Baa! Baa!'

Mister Horse, how do you say to the Lord, 'I love you?'
Mister Horse, how do you say to the Lord, 'I love you?'
'Well I stand around in the field all day,
and it gives me plenty of time to say:
Neigh! Neigh! Neigh!'

Mister Chicken, how do you say to the Lord, 'I love you?'
Mister Chicken, how do you say to the Lord, 'I love you?'
'Well I peck around in the yard all day,
and it gives me plenty of time to say:
Cluck! Cluck! Cluck!'

Mister Pig, how do you say to the Lord, 'I love you?'
Mister Pig, how do you say to the Lord, 'I love you?'
'Well I roll around in the mud all day,
and it gives me plenty of time to say:
Oink! Oink! Oink!'

*Continued overleaf*

Mister Fish, how do you say to the Lord,
'I love you?'
Mister Fish, how do you say to the Lord,
'I love you?'
'Well I swim around in the pond all day,
and it gives me plenty of time to say:
Pop! Pop! Pop!'

Mister Duck, how do you say to the
Lord, 'I love you?'
Mister Duck, how do you say to the
Lord, 'I love you?'
'Well I swim around in the pond all day,
and it gives me plenty of time to say:
Quack! Quack! Quack!'



## 254 Jim Bailey

Moses went down to see Pharaoh,
he said, 'Let my people go'.
Moses went down to see Pharaoh,
all Pharaoh could say was 'no'.
Moses turned his staff to a snake, oh,
he turned the Nile into blood.
'Pharaoh be fair, oh let my people go.'
Pharaoh said 'no' when he shouldn't have.

Moses went down to see Pharaoh,
Pharaoh not in a good mood.
He told Moses to 'hop it', and that
'Moses, you're going to get sued'.
Moses gave him a flea in the ear,
bugged him, got under his skin.
Pharaoh he cried, 'Pass the insecticide'.
Moses laughed, there were no flies on him.

*Pharaoh, let God's people go,*
*will you ever know,*
*God his pow'r will show?*
*Pharaoh will you ever learn?*
*Have you never heard,*
*God has the last word?*

Moses went down to see Pharaoh,
Pharaoh was not very pleased.
Pharaoh he came to boiling point,
when Egypt got mad cow disease.
But God, through Moses, wasn't finished
and, afflicted with terrible sores,
Pharaoh was to see God was bigger
than he,
and that it never rains, it just pours.

Moses went down to see Pharaoh,
'Hail, Pharaoh,' he said, tongue in cheek.
'The locusts are coming to finish the job
and devour all there is left to eat.
Then darkness will cover the land oh,
just because you couldn't see.
Your firstborn will die, due to your
stubborn pride,
and my people they will be set free.



## 255 Traditional

*My God is so big, so strong and*
*so mighty,*
*there's nothing that he cannot do.*
*My God is so big, so strong and*
*so mighty,*
*there's nothing that he cannot do.*

The rivers are his, the mountains are his,
the stars are his handiwork too.

He's called you to live for him ev'ry day,
in all that you say and you do.

## 256 Ian Smale

My God shall supply all my needs,
my God shall supply all my needs,
my God shall supply all my needs,
'cause it says so in the Bible.

*'Cause it says so (where?)*
*in the book that came from heav'n,*
*'cause it says so (where?)*
*Isaiah fifty-eight elev'n.*
*My God shall supply all my needs,*
*'cause it says so in the Bible.*



## 257 Darlene Zschech

My Jesus, my Saviour,
Lord, there is none like you.
All of my days
I want to praise
the wonders of your mighty love.
My comfort, my shelter,
tower of refuge and strength,
let ev'ry breath,
all that I am,
never cease to worship you.

*Shout to the Lord, all the earth,*
*let us sing*
*power and majesty, praise to the King.*
*Mountains bow down and the seas*
*will roar*
*at the sound of your name.*
*I sing for joy*
*at the work of your hands.*
*For ever I'll love you, for ever I'll*
*stand.*
*Nothing compares to the promise I*
*have in you.*



## 258 Noel and Tricia Richards

*My lips shall praise you, my great*
*Redeemer;*
*my heart will worship, Almighty*
*Saviour.*

You take all my guilt away,
turn the darkest night to brightest
day;
you are the restorer of my soul.

Love that conquers ev'ry fear,
in the midst of trouble you draw near;
you are the restorer of my soul.

You're the source of happiness,
bringing peace when I am in distress;
you are the restorer of my soul.



## 259 Judy MacKenzie Dunn

My rock (my rock),
my rock (my rock),
you are (you are)
my strong foundation;
my rock (my rock),
my rock (my rock),
you are (you are)
my one salvation;
in you, oh Lord,
I will put my trust;
blessed be the Lord my rock.



## 260 Capt. Alan Price, CA

Na na na na na,
na na na na na na na na na.

*There's a place waiting for me,*
*a place that's good to be,*
*I know, 'cos Jesus said it!*
*There's a place waiting for me,*
*a place that's good to be,*
*I know, 'cos Jesus said it!*

*Continued overleaf*

He went to get it ready
for all who follow him;
I know, 'cos Jesus said it!
It's in his Father's house,
a house with many rooms;
it's true, 'cos Jesus said it!
If he went to get it ready,
he surely will return,
it's true, 'cos Jesus said it!
And when the time is right,
he'll take us there with him,
it's true, 'cos Jesus said it!



## 261 Capt. Alan Price, CA

Nobody liked Zacchaeus,
the small man from Jericho;
ev'ryone thought he was rotten,
Zacchaeus, he hated it so.

Now Zack, he heard about Jesus,
he climbed up a tree for a view;
said Jesus, 'I'm coming to your house
today;
Zacchaeus, I'm talking to you!'

*Oh, you'd better get off your back, Zack,*
*you'd better come down from the tree;*
*no matter what others may think of you,*
*to Jesus you're special, you see!*

Because of the visit of Jesus,
Zacchaeus became someone new;
he gave four times as much as he'd
cheated,
and half of his wealth away, too!

You might not be quite like Zacchaeus,
but sometimes you may feel quite blue.
The Bible is clear about one thing;
Jesus loves people like you!

Final chorus:
*Oh, you'd better get off your back,*
*Whack,*
*you'd better just listen to me;*
*no matter what others may think of you,*
*to Jesus you're special, you see!*



## 262 Capt. Alan Price, CA

Now I belong to Jesus and his Spirit
lives in me,
I'm a soldier and a servant for the King
of kings.
I'll fight against the wrong I find,
I'll serve him with my heart and mind,
a soldier and a servant I will be.
Make me faithful, Lord Jesus,
make me faithful, Lord, to you.
Keep me faithful, Lord Jesus,
keep me faithful, Lord, to you.



## 263 Sammy Horner

*Obey the maker's instructions all the*
*time.*
*Obey the maker's instructions and you*
*will find;*
*obey the maker's instructions will help*
*you see,*
*that things fit together much more easily.*

So you can buy a model
of your favourite classic car,
without reading instructions
you put it together so far;
but when you think you're finished
you find a little extra bit,
it's the driver of the car
but now he just won't fit.

Say that you read the Bible
to see what God has said,
and you find instructions
and store them in your head;
but when you find that you're
tempted
to doing things the wrong way,
instructions mean nothing
unless you do what they say.



## 264 Mike Burn

Oh, I'm fighting, but not against
people,
it's a battle of good and evil;
but I don't need a gun, I don't need a
sword,
I don't need sticks and I don't need
stones.
My weapons are not of this world.
I'll fight with a prayer of faith,
I'll fight with a shout of praise;
my weapon is the Word of God.
It's sharper than any sword,
it cuts through the darkness of this
world,
and the enemy's walls come crashing
down,
as God's kingdom gets built.



## 265 Steve Burnhope

Oh, it's so good to know,
oh, it's so good.
Oh, it's so good to know
Jesus loves me.
*(Repeat)*

He loves me so much,
he came to earth for me.
He loves me so much,
that he died for me.
But he came back to life again in victory,
all because he loves me.
Oh, it's so good to know,
oh, it's so good to know,
oh, it's so good to know
Jesus loves me.



## 266 Unknown

*Oh! Oh! Oh! how good is the Lord,*
*Oh! Oh! Oh! how good is the Lord,*
*Oh! Oh! Oh! how good is the Lord,*
*I never will forget what he has done*
*for me.*

He gives me salvation,
how good is the Lord,
he gives me salvation,
how good is the Lord,
he gives me salvation,
how good is the Lord,
I never will forget
what he has done for me.

He gives me his blessings . . .

He gives me his Spirit . . .

He gives me his healing . . .

He gives me his glory . . .

*Other verses may be added as*
*appropriate*

## 267 Roger Jones

Oh, once there was a father,
who had two sons at home.
The young one wanted money,
so he could start to roam.

*Lost! Lost! Lost and found!*
*That's what the Bible said!*
*Lost! Lost! Lost and found!*
*The son back from the dead.*

He left home one bright morning,
he said, 'I must be free!
I'll go to the far country,
there's marv'lous sights to see!

He started spending money
on women, wine and song;
but this great time of plenty,
it didn't last too long!

He soon found he was starving,
the pigs he had to feed;
when he was back with father,
he never had a need!

He started back to father,
ashamed and all alone;
but father saw him coming,
and welcomed him back home!



## 268 Graham Kendrick

*Leader* *Oh, the Lord is good;*
*All* *oh, the Lord is good!*
*Leader* *The Lord is good;*
*All* *the Lord is good!*

*Leader* We want to hear you testify:
*All* oh, the Lord is good.
*Leader* We want to hear you say:
*All* the Lord is good.
*Leader* We want to hear it loud and strong:
*All* oh, the Lord is good.
*Leader* We want to hear you shout:
*All* the Lord is good!

*Leader* We want to hear the children say:
*All* oh, the Lord is good.
*Leader* We want to hear you say:
*All* the Lord is good.
*Leader* We want to hear you loud and strong:
*All* oh, the Lord is good.
*Leader* We want to hear you shout:
*All* the Lord is good!

*Leader* We want to hear the brothers say:
*All* oh, the Lord is good.
*Leader* We want to hear you say:
*All* the Lord is good.
*Leader* We want to hear the sisters say:
*All* oh, the Lord is good.
*Leader* We want to hear you say:
*All* the Lord is good.

*Leader* The younger to the older say:
*Younger* oh, the Lord is good.
*Leader* We want to hear you say:
*Younger* the Lord is good.
*Leader* Older to the younger say:
*Older* oh, the Lord is good.
*Leader* We want to hear you say:
*Older* the Lord is good.

*Leader* Let every generation say:
*All* oh, the Lord is good.

| | |
|---|---|
| *Leader* | We want to hear you say: |
| *All* | the Lord is good, |
| *Leader* | so good, |
| *All* | so good; |
| *Leader* | so kind, |
| *All* | so kind; |
| *Leader* | give him glory, |
| *All* | give him glory, |
| *Leader* | all the time, |
| *All* | all the time. |



## 269 Doug Horley

*Oi, oi, we are gonna praise the Lord.*
*Oi, oi, we are gonna praise the Lord.*
*Oi, oi, we are gonna praise the Lord.*
*He's an exciting, powerising, c-colossal,*
*humungousmungous*
(Repeat)
*God!*

But it's sometimes hard to understand
that the God who made the earth and man
would point a finger down from heaven
and shout:
'Hey you! I love you. Hey you! I love you.
Hey you, you! I love you.' – but it's true!'



## 270 Ian Smale

O Lord, you're great, you are fabulous,
we love you more than any words can
sing, sing, sing.
O Lord, you're great, you are so generous,
you lavish us with gifts when we don't
deserve a thing.

*Allelu, alleluia, praise you, Lord.*
*Alleluia, praise you, Lord.*
*Alleluia, praise you, Lord.*
(Repeat)

Oh Lord, you're great, you are so
powerful,
you hold the mighty universe in your
hand, hand, hand.
Oh Lord, you're great, you are so
beautiful,
you've poured out your love on this
undeserving land.



## 271 A. W. Edsor

On Calvary's tree he died for me,
that I his love might know.
To set me free he died for me,
that's why I love him so.



## 272 Ian White

Once there was a house, a busy little
house,
and this is all about the busy little house.

Jesus Christ had come, teaching
ev'ryone,
so ev'ryone has run to the busy little
house.

Ev'ryone was there, you couldn't find a
chair,
in fact you had to fight for air in the
busy little house.

A man who couldn't walk was carried to
the spot,
but the place was chock-a-block in the
busy little house.

Whatever shall we do, whatever shall we
do?
We'll never get him through into the
busy little house.

*Continued overleaf*

We'll open up the roof, we'll open up the roof,
and then we'll put him through into the busy little house.

Then Jesus turned his eyes, and saw to his surprise
the man coming from the skies into the busy little house.

Then Jesus turned and said, 'Get up and take your bed,
and run along instead from the busy little house.'



## 273 Sydney Carter

One more step along the world I go,
one more step along the world I go.
From the old things to the new,
keep me travelling along with you.

*And it's from the old I travel to the new,*
*keep me travelling along with you.*

Round the corners of the world I turn,
more and more about the world I learn.
All the new things that I see
you'll be looking at along with me.

As I travel through the bad and good,
keep me travelling the way I should.
Where I see no way to go,
you'll be telling me the way, I know.

Give me courage when the world is rough,
keep me loving though the world is tough.
Leap and sing in all I do,
keep me travelling along with you.

You are older than the world can be,
you are younger than the life in me.
Ever old and ever new,
keep me travelling along with you.



## 274 Lisa Mazak

*One, two, three, Jesus loves me.*
*One, two, Jesus loves you.*

Three, four, he loves you more
than you've ever been loved before.

Five, six, seven, we're going to heav'n.
Eight, nine, it's truly divine.

Nine, ten, it's time to end;*
but instead we'll sing it again

* *Last time*
There's no time to sing it again.



## 275 Judy MacKenzie Dunn

Only one of me,
only one of you,
only one of ev'ryone,
incredible but true.
Millions of us all,
none of us the same,
but God knows ev'ry single face
and ev'ry single name.

*Because he's so great, only God can do it,*
*so great, that's why we sing.*
*So great, I wish ev'rybody knew it,*
*so great, that's why we worship him.*

Ev'ry thought I think,
ev'ry prayer I pray,
ev'ry cry I cry to him and ev'rything
I say,
in a world that's full of words
that swirl in space and time,
God's tuned in to all of them,
he knows which ones are mine.



## 276 Yvonne Scott

On my bed I remember you,
I remember you, O God.
On my bed I remember you,
you are my help.

*And I will praise you as long as I live,*
*and I will lift up my hands.*
*And I will praise you as long as I live,*
*and I will lift up my hands.*

When I wake I remember you,
I remember you, O God.
When I wake I remember you,
you are my help.

When I eat I remember you,
I remember you, O God.
When I eat I remember you,
you are my help.

When I play I remember you,
I remember you, O God.
When I play I remember you,
you are my help.



## 277 Ian Smale

On my tiptoes I am tall,
when I crouch down I am so small,
I stretch my hands out then I'm wide,
Jesus made me special.

Jesus loves me when I'm tall,
Jesus loves me when I'm small,
Jesus loves me when I'm wide,
Jesus made me special.

S - P - E - C - I - A - L,
S - P - E - C - I - A - L,
S - P - E - C - I - A - L,
Jesus made me special.



## 278 Robert Cull

Open our eyes, Lord,
we want to see Jesus,
to reach out and touch him
and say that we love him;
Open our ears, Lord,
and help us to listen;
O open our eyes, Lord,
we want to see Jesus!



## 279 Martin Smith

Over the mountains and the sea
your river runs with love for me,
and I will open up my heart
and let the Healer set me free.
I'm happy to be in the truth,
and I will daily lift my hands,
for I will always sing of
when your love came down.

*I could sing of your love for ever,*
*I could sing of your love for ever,*
*I could sing of your love for ever,*
*I could sing of your love for ever.*

O, I feel like dancing,
it's foolishness, I know;
but when the world has seen the light,
they will dance with joy
like we're dancing now.

## 280 Capt. Alan Price, CA

People brought children to Jesus,
to Jesus, to Jesus;
people brought children to Jesus,
to be touched by him.

But the disciples tried to stop them,
to stop them, to stop them;
but the disciples tried to stop them,
but they got it wrong!

Jesus was angry and he shouted,
he shouted, he shouted!
Jesus was angry and he shouted,
'Let them come to me!'

Jesus took the children in his arms,
in his arms, in his arms;
Jesus took the children in his arms,
gave them each a hug!

Jesus, please, I ask you, will you hug me
too!
hug me too! hug me too!
Jesus, please, I ask you, will you hug me
too,
for I am your child!

Hallelujah, hallelujah, hallelu!
Hallelu, hallelu!
Hallelujah, hallelujah, hallelu!
Jesus loves me!



## 281 Unknown

Peter and John went to pray,
they met a lame man on the way.
He asked for alms and held out his palms,
and this is what Peter did say:

'Silver and gold have I none,
but such as I have I give you;
in the name of Jesus Christ of Nazareth,
rise up and walk!'

He went walking and leaping and
praising God,
walking and leaping and praising God.
'In the name of Jesus Christ of Nazareth,
rise up and walk.'



## 282 Capt. Alan Price, CA

*Please fill me, Lord, with your power,*
*pow'r to live for you;*
*Holy Spirit, ev'ry hour,*
*let your love flow through.*

When you died on Calvary,
I know it was in love for me.
Lord, I know your loving care
is for people ev'rywhere.

Lord, I want to live for you,
live the way you want me to,
do the things that make you glad,
not the things that make you sad.



## 283 Andy Piercy and Dave Clifton

*Praise God from whom all blessings flow,*
*praise him, all creatures here below.*
*Praise him above, you heav'nly host,*
*praise Father, Son and Holy Ghost.*
(Repeat)

Give glory to the Father,
give glory to the Son,
give glory to the Spirit
while endless ages run.
'Worthy the Lamb,' all heaven cries,
'to be exalted thus.'
'Worthy the Lamb,' our hearts reply,
'for he was slain for us.'

Praise God from whom all blessings flow.
Praise God from whom all blessings flow.
Praise God from whom all blessings flow.
Praise God from whom all blessings flow.



## 284 John Kennett

Praise him on the trumpet,
the psaltery and harp,
praise him on the timbrel
and the dance;
praise him with stringed instruments too.
Praise him on the loud cymbals,
praise him on the loud cymbals,
let ev'rything that has breath
praise the Lord.

Hallelujah, praise the Lord,
hallelujah, praise the Lord,
let ev'rything that has breath
praise the Lord.
*(Repeat)*



## 285 Mike Burn

Pray at all times, never ceasing,
ask for what you need with
thanksgiving.
Join together in agreement
and together we'll see the kingdom
come.

Give thanks to the Father,
for he hears all our prayers.
Give thanks to the Son,
for he prays for us.
Give thanks to the Spirit,
for when we don't know how to pray
he will plead with God on our behalf.



## 286 Paul Crouch and David Mudie

Prayer is like a telephone
for us to talk to Jesus.
Prayer is like a telephone
for us to talk to God.
Prayer is like a telephone
for us to talk to Jesus.
Pick it up and use it ev'ry day.
We can shout out loud,
we can whisper softly,
we can make no noise at all,
but he'll always hear our call.



## 287 Roger Jones

Riding high and low,
looking for a king,
riding over deserts,
with the gifts we bring.

*Frankincense and myrrh,*
*gold we bring to him,*
*these are what we'll give,*
*and our hearts to him.*

Over mountains high,
over deserts dry,
on to find this baby,
looking in the sky!

*Continued overleaf*

*Frankincense and myrrh,*
*gold we bring to him,*
*these are what we'll give,*
*and our hearts to him.*

On we go to Herod,
but he'll turn so green,
when we tell of Jesus,
and the star we've seen.

We are nearly there,
might get there today;
star is still above us,
showing us the way.



## 288 Unknown

*Rise, and shine, and give God the glory, glory.*
*Rise, and shine, and give God the glory, glory.*
*Rise, and shine, and give God the glory, glory,*
*children of the Lord.*

The Lord said to Noah: 'There's gonna be a floody, floody.'
Lord said to Noah: 'There's gonna be a floody, floody.
Get those children out of the muddy, muddy,
children of the Lord.'

The Lord told Noah to build him an arky, arky,
Lord told Noah to build him an arky, arky.
Build it out of gopher barky, barky,
children of the Lord.

The animals, the animals, they came on, by twosies, twosies,
animals, the animals, they came on, by twosies, twosies.
Elephants and kangaroosies, 'roosies,
children of the Lord.

It rained and poured for forty daysies, daysies,
rained and poured for forty daysies, daysies.
Almost drove those animals crazies, crazies,
children of the Lord.

The sun came out and dried up the landy, landy,
sun came out and dried up the landy, landy.
Ev'rything was fine and dandy, dandy,
children of the Lord.

## 289 Mark and Helen Johnson

*Risen! Risen! Jesus is risen!*
*The Spirit was given, Jesus is alive!**

Early in the morning, on the first day of the week,
women went to visit at the tomb;
angels came and told them: 'The one you've come to see,
he isn't here, but you will meet him soon!'

Fearful and excited, amazed by all they'd seen,
Mary and her friends ran from the tomb:
finding the disciples together where they'd meet,
bursting with joy, they ran into the room!

Two of the believers, with thoughts about the week,
walked the road so lonely and confused.
While they spoke of Jesus, and all he'd come to mean,
he came along beside them with the news.

All of his disciples were terrified to see
Jesus before them in the room.
'Why are you so frightened?' he said, 'It's really me!
All of the things I told you have come true!'

*Last time
*Risen! Risen! Jesus is risen!*



## 290 Paul Field

*Safe in the Father's hands,*
*we are safe in the Father's hands.*
*There may be things we don't understand,*
*we're safe in the Father's hands.*

So many things we'll never learn,
no matter how hard we try.
Though we may feel small,
the maker of all watches with loving eyes.

Trusting in God, we can be sure
no matter where life may lead,
his promises told, he's in control,
he's ev'rything we need.



## 291 Michael Perry

See him lying on a bed of straw,
a draughty stable with an open door.
Mary cradling the babe she bore:
the Prince of Glory is his name.

*Oh, now carry me to Bethlehem,*
*to see the Lord of love again:*
*just as poor as was the stable then,*
*the Prince of Glory when he came!*

Star of silver, sweep across the skies,
show where Jesus in a manger lies;
shepherds, swiftly from your stupor rise
to see the Saviour of the world!

Angels, sing again the song you sang,
sing the story of God's gracious plan;
sing that Bethl'em's little baby can
be the Saviour of us all.

Mine are riches from your poverty;
from your innocence, eternity;
mine, forgiveness by your death for me,
child of sorrow for my joy.



## 292 Karen Lafferty

Seek ye first the kingdom of God
and his righteousness,
and all these things shall be added unto you,
hallelu, hallelujah!

*Hallelujah! Hallelujah!*
*Hallelujah! Hallelu, hallelujah!*

You shall not live by bread alone,
but by every word
that proceeds from the mouth of God,
hallelu, hallelujah!

*Continued overleaf*

*Hallelujah! Hallelujah!*
*Hallelujah! Hallelu, hallelujah!*

Ask and it shall be given unto you,
seek and you shall find.
Knock and it shall be opened unto you,
hallelu, hallelujah.

If the Son shall set you free,
you shall be free indeed.
You shall know the truth and the truth
shall set you free,
hallelu, hallelujah!

Let your light so shine before men
that they may see your good works
and glorify your Father in heaven,
hallelu, hallelujah!

Trust in the Lord with all your heart,
he shall direct your paths,
in all your ways acknowledge him,
hallelu, hallelujah!



## 293 David Graham

Shake a friend's hand,
shake a hand next to ya,
shake a friend's hand and sing la la;
shake a friend's hand,
shake a hand next to ya,
shake a friend's hand and sing,
sing a la la la la la laleluia,
la la la la laleluia.
La la la la la laleluia,
la la la la laleluia!

Hug a friend's neck,
hug a neck next to ya . . .

Squeeze a friend's knee,
squeeze a knee next to ya . . .

Scratch a friend's back,
scratch a back next to ya . . .

Jesus is a friend,
he's a friend next to ya . . .

Don't just stand in your own little place,
reach out and touch a friend.
Give of yourself and you will find
the blessings never end!



## 294 Andrew and Pauline Pearson

Shake those hands,
wiggle those feet,
nod that head,
in case it's still asleep.
*(Repeat)*

*Wake up and praise the Lord,*
*wake up and praise the Lord,*
*wake up and praise the Lord*
*with all of me.*



## 295 Paul Crouch and David Mudie

Shoop shoop doobee doo doo,
there's nobody who loves me like
you do.
Shoop shoop doobee doo doo,
nobody's a friend like you.

Wop bop doobee doo waa,
we sing your name and shout
hallelujah.
Wop bop doobee doo waa,
King of kings for ever you are!

Shoop shoop doobee doo doo,
I shout your name and sing hallelujah.
Shoop shoop doobee doo doo,
only you can make my life new.

Wop bop doobee doo waa,
we sing your name and shout
hallelujah.
Wop bop doobee doo waa,
King of kings for ever you are.

Shoop shoop doobee doo doo,
you're ev'rything that ever was true now.
Shoop shoop doobee doo doo,
I want to tell my friends about you.

Wop bop doobee doo waa,
we sing your name and shout
hallelujah.
Wop bop doobee doo waa,
King of kings for ever you are!



## 296 Chris Jackson

*Sing and shout your praise to our God,*
*he alone is King.*
*He's the ruler of the earth,*
*he's the Lord of ev'rything.*

He is a mighty God,
full of majesty,
glory and honour and pow'r.
So come and praise him,
shout aloud,
lift his name on high.

The Lord is merciful,
loving and kind;
faithful and gentle is he.
So come and worship him,
bow the knee,
magnify his name with me.



## 297 Mark and Helen Johnson

Sing a song, sing a joyful song,
sing a joyful song to celebrate!
Sing a song, sing a joyful song,
sing a joyful song to celebrate!

*Jesus is alive, you know,*
*he's risen from the dead!*
*He was crucified*
*but now he's risen like he said.*
*(Hallelujah!)*

Clap your hands, clap your hands like this,
clap your hands like this to celebrate!
Clap your hands, clap your hands like this,
clap your hands like this to celebrate!

Jump up and down, up and down and
around,
up and down and around to celebrate!
Jump up and down, up and down and
around,
up and down and around to celebrate!

Dance to the beat, to the beat of the
drum,
to the beat of the drum to celebrate!
Dance to the beat, to the beat of the
drum,
to the beat of the drum to celebrate!

Wave your hands, wave your hands in
the air,
wave your hands in the air to celebrate!
Wave your hands, wave your hands in
the air,
wave your hands in the air to celebrate!

Sing a song, sing a joyful song,
sing a joyful song to celebrate!
Sing a song, sing a joyful song,
sing a joyful song to celebrate!

## 298 Derek Llewellyn

Sing praise to God the Father,
God the Spirit, God the Son.
Sing praise to God who loves us,
praise him ev'ryone.

Sing praise to God the Father,
clap your hands and jump for joy.
He made the world around us,
and he loves us all.

Sing praise to God's Son Jesus,
clap your hands and jump for joy.
Wave your arms and turn around.
He teaches us about the Father,
and he loves us all.

Sing praise to the Holy Spirit,
clap your hands and jump for joy.
Wave your arms and jump around,
stamp your feet and shout hooray.
He helps us to live like Jesus
and he loves us all.



## 299 Ian Smale

So if you think you're standing firm,
be careful you don't fall;
so if you think you're standing firm,
be careful you don't fall;
so if you think you're standing firm,
be careful you don't fall;
so if you think you're standing firm,
be careful you don't fall.



## 300 Nick Harding

*So I'll trust (so I'll trust)*
*in God (in God),*
*wherever I am,*
*I know I can,*
*so I'll trust (so I'll trust),*
*in God (in God),*
*'cos God has got a plan,*
*God has got a plan.*

God was, God is and always will be.
He knows what I hear and do and see.
He made me, loves me, leads me too.
He's got a plan for me and you.

God was, and God is with me here,
he sent his Son, he takes my fear,
his Spirit lives deep in my heart –
I'm in his plan right from the start.



## 301 Ian Smale

*So I've made up my mind,*
*that I'm gonna follow him,*
*wherever Jesus leads me I will go.*
(Repeat)

I may be scared
by the things I see,
but Jesus won't
let them destroy me.

I may be scared
by the things I hear,
but Jesus won't
let me live in fear.

I may be scared
by the things I know,
but Jesus won't
ever let me go.

## 302 Capt. Alan Price, CA

Some people are fat, some people are thin,
but we've all got a problem with a thing called sin;
some people are pink, some people are brown,
but no matter what the colour, we're the same deep down!

*No matter who we are,*
*God loves us ev'ry one;*
*to make us his friends again,*
*he gave his only Son.*

Some people we like, some people we don't,
but how can we love our neighbour if try we won't?
God's help is at hand, we just need to ask,
and God the Holy Spirit will help us in the task.



## 303 Sammy Horner

Some people laugh, some people sing,
some people clap, and so they bring
their worship to the King of kings.
What do you do? What do you do?

Some people dance, some bring a word,
some people cry before the Lord,
and so they bring their worship to
the King of kings, the King of kings.

Some people march and raise their hands,
and some are quiet, but understand
there are many ways of worshipping
the King of kings, the King of kings.



## 304 Paul Field

Some things make you angry and some things can make you shout;
sometimes you can't keep it in, you've got to let it out;
but before you lose your temper, stop!
Count to ten and say a prayer for love.

*Count to ten and say a prayer,*
*Jesus always will be there,*
*count to ten and talk to him,*
*let him put his love within* your heart.*
*One, two, three, four, five,*
*six, seven, eight, nine, ten.*

Angry words can hurt someone much more than sticks or stones,
so when you feel your temper rising to the danger zone,
close your eyes and keep your lips shut tight,
count to ten and say a prayer for love.

* Last time
*Say a prayer for love.*



## 305 Chris Mercer

Sometimes in the morning
I feel sad, sad, sad,
so I just ask Jesus,
make my sad heart glad.

*Wake up and dance for joy,*
*wake up and dance for joy,*
*wake up and dance for joy,*
*first thing in the morning.*

Sometimes in the morning,
I feel glad, glad, glad,
so I just praise Jesus,
for the day I'll have.

## 306 Ian Smale

So we're marching along, singing a song,
we're in the Lord's army.
We're fighting for right as we're learning what's wrong,
'cause we're in the Lord's army.
He's got the victory, so let's really shout,
we're in the Lord's army.
We're in the Lord's (yeah),
we're in the Lord's (right),
we're in the Lord's army.



## 307 Chris Jackson

Speak, Lord, I am your servant,
I am list'ning to your voice.
Speak, Lord, I am your servant,
I am list'ning.



## 308 Capt. Alan Price, CA

*Special agents, we're special agents,*
*for J - E - S - U - S.*
*He called us and we said 'yes',*
*we'll be his special agents,*
*special agents.*

We're special 'cos we know his care,
a love that's so tremendous.
We're agents for Jesus the King,
'cos he's the one who sends us!

We'll use our eyes to see just where
God is working around us.
We'll use our ears to listen, too,
and act on what he tells us!



## 309 Judy Bailey

*Spirit (Spirit),*
*Holy Spirit (Holy Spirit),*
*fall on me.*
*Spirit (Spirit),*
*Holy Spirit (Holy Spirit),*
*fall on me.*

I want to know that your presence is near,
I want to know that your power is here.
I want the weight of your glory to fall on me,
so come now Holy . . .

*Spirit (Spirit) . . .*

*We welcome you here,*
*we welcome you here,*
*we welcome you here,*
*we need you, we need you.*

I want to know that you're here in this place,
healing our lives and enlarging our faith.
I want to know when I leave there's a change in me,
so come now Holy . . .

*Spirit (Spirit) . . .*

*We welcome you . . .*



## 310 Mark and Helen Johnson

Sun and the moon and the starlit sky,
God created them all.
Rivers and seas and the oceans wide,
he created them all.
Forests and fields and the deserts dry,
God created them all.
Valleys and foothills and mountains high,
he created them all.

*God looked down from heaven,*
*he was pleased, oh yeah!*
*Ev'rything was just as it should be,*
*ah ha!**

Every creature that moves and breathes,
God created them all.
Fliers and swimmers and some with feet,
he created them all.
Beautiful flowers and fruitful trees,
God created them all.
Every plant that you'll ever see,
he created them all.

Summer and autumn and winter, spring,
God created them all.
Each of the changes the seasons bring,
he created them all.
Thunder and lightning, the rain and wind,
God created them all.
Glorious sunsets and snowy scenes,
he created them all.

* Last time
God created the whole wide world, he
created it all!



## 311 Ian White

S - U - N is shining in the sky,
S - U - N is shining in the sky,
bringing light, bringing light all around.
*(Repeat)*

But S - O - N, the Son who came to die,
S - O - N, the Son who came to die,
bringing life, bringing life all around.

And if you have the Son you have life,
oh, if you have the Son you have life,
oh, if you have the Son you have life,
you have life in abundance.



## 312 Graham Kendrick and Steve Thompson

*Teach me to dance*
*to the beat of your heart,*
*teach me to move*
*in the pow'r of your Spirit,*
*teach me to walk*
*in the light of your presence,*
*teach me to dance*
*to the beat of your heart.*
*Teach me to love*
*with your heart of compassion,*
*teach me to trust*
*in the word of your promise,*
*teach me to hope*
*in the day of your coming,*
*teach me to dance*
*to the beat of your heart.*

You wrote the rhythm of life,
created heaven and earth,
in you is joy without measure.
So, like a child in your sight,
I dance to see your delight,
for I was made for your pleasure,
pleasure.

Let all my movements express
a heart that loves to say 'yes',
a will that leaps to obey you.
Let all my energy blaze
to see the joy in your face;
let my whole being praise you,
praise you.



## 313 Unknown

*Thank you, Jesus, thank you, Jesus,*
*thank you, Lord, for loving me.*
*Thank you, Jesus, thank you, Jesus,*
*thank you, Lord, for loving me.*

*Continued overleaf*

You went to Calvary,
and there you died for me.
Thank you, Lord, for loving me.
*(Repeat)*

*Thank you, Jesus, thank you, Jesus,*
*thank you, Lord, for loving me.*
*Thank you, Jesus, thank you, Jesus,*
*thank you, Lord, for loving me.*

You rose up from the grave,
to me new life you gave,
thank you, Lord, for loving me.
*(Repeat)*

You're coming back again,
and we with you shall reign.
Thank you, Lord, for loving me.
*(Repeat)*

## 314 Capt. Alan Price, CA

*Thank you very much!*
*Thank you very much!*
*Thank you very much for all you do for me!*
*Thank you very much!*
*Thank you very much!*
*Thank you very much for all you mean to me!*

There's so many things I often take for granted,
things I hardly think about,
I just know that they're there!
But I want to take the time to tell you that I'm grateful.
Thank you for the many things that prove you really care!



## 315 John MacPherson

The blessing of God be upon you
and around you, wherever you go.
The blessing of God be within you
and among you, wherever you go.
Wherever you go, whatever you do,
may the blessing of God go with you.



## 316 Doug Horley

The gift of God is eternal life through Jesus Christ,
the gift of God is eternal life through Jesus Christ,
the gift of God is eternal life through Jesus Christ,
through Jesus, Jesus Christ.
Jesus is the boss of my life,
he's the only one can make it come right;
Jesus is the boss of my life, Jesus is the boss.

*Leader* I'm a friend of Jesus Christ,
*All* I'm a friend of Jesus Christ.
*Leader* He's God's Son and he's alive,
*All* he's God's Son and he's alive.
*Leader* I will trust in him, it's true,
*All* I will trust in him, it's true.
*Leader* He's always there to see me through,
*All* he's always there to see me through.
*Leader* Sound off –
*All* Jesus,
*Leader* Sound off –
*All* is Lord.
*Leader* Sound off –
*All* Jesus,
*Leader* Sound off –
*All* is Lord!

*Rap*
I said, come on ev'rybody and move
your feet,
the rhythm is hot, it's a powerful beat.
The time is right to do some business,
get on your feet and be a witness
to the Holy One,
the King of kings, God's only Son.
Jesus Christ, that's his name,
he died to take our sin and shame.



## 317 Capt. Alan Price, CA

The joy of the Lord is a great thing,
quite different from anything I know.
Jesus in my life makes my heart sing,
despite the things that make me feel
quite low.
It's a joy from deep inside, only Jesus
can provide,
I'm gonna let the joy of Jesus overflow!
It's a joy from deep inside, only Jesus
can provide,
I'm gonna let the joy of Jesus overflow!



## 318 Richard Hubbard

The promise of the Holy Spirit
is for you.
The promise of the Holy Spirit
is for your children.
The promise of the Holy Spirit
is for all who are far off,
even as many as the Lord your God
shall call.
Oh yeah!
Acts, chapter two, verse thirty-nine.



## 319 Paul Crouch and David Mudie

The race that we are running
may be hard, it may be tough,
But in his word God promised
that his strength would be enough
to see us to the finish line,
and there to claim the prize
that Jesus died to win for us –
resurrection life.

We're running, we're running,
we're focused on the goal.
We're pressing on,
we're getting there,
we will not trip and fall.
We're running, we're running,
we'll put our trust in him.
Even though it's tough we know
God will help us win.



## 320 John Gowans

There are hundreds of sparrows,
thousands, millions,
they're two a penny, far too many there
must be;
there are hundreds and thousands,
millions of sparrows,
but God knows ev'ry one, and God
knows me.

There are hundreds of flowers,
thousands, millions,
and flowers fair the meadows wear for
all to see;
there are hundreds and thousands,
millions of flowers,
but God knows ev'ry one, and God
knows me.

*Continued overleaf*

There are hundreds of planets,
thousands, millions,
way out in space each has a place by
God's decree;
there are hundreds and thousands,
millions of planets,
but God knows ev'ry one, and God
knows me.

There are hundreds of children,
thousands, millions,
and yet their names are written on God's
memory,
there are hundreds and thousands,
millions of children,
but God knows ev'ry one, and God
knows me.



## 321 Steve Burnhope

There are lots of ways that I can praise,
there are very many things that I can do;
there are lots of ways that I can praise,
and show you, Lord, how much I love
you.
I can touch my toes, I can hold my nose,
I can crouch down low, I can jump up
high.
I can clap like this, I can do the twist,
but the thing that I do best is shout, 'I
love you, Lord!'



## 322 Capt. Alan Price, CA

There are so many stories that I love to
hear,
I picture the scenes in my head.
In books or on TV they also appear,
I think of them all in my head.
But the stories of Jesus are different you
see,
'cos he's a real person who loves you
and me.
Though I can't see him, I know he is real;
Jesus is my best friend.

*So tell me the stories of Jesus,*
*over and over and over again;*
*tell me the stories of Jesus,*
*over and over again.*

There are so many stories that I love to
hear,
I picture the scenes in my head.
In books or on TV they also appear,
I think of them all in my head.
But the story of Jesus is different I know,
'cos he's a real person who lived long
ago.
Though he's in heaven, his Spirit is here,
that's how he's my best friend.



## 323 Doug Horley, Belinda Horley and Penny Roberts

*There is a God who knows your name,*
*there is a God who feels your pain;*
*there is a love holding out for you,*
*don't turn away, let him love you.*

'Cos he loves you with a passion, an
endless raging fire,
from eternity to eternity you are his
heart's desire.
And if you could for a moment glimpse
the hugeness of his heart,
you'd see how he simply loves you.

He loves you with a passion, he's always
on your side,
like a mighty wave that won't be
stopped, his love is ocean wide.
Higher than the heavens above, and
deeper than the sea;
truth is, just this, he simply loves you.

When you feel you've fallen far too far to
ever stand again,
and you can't believe this Holy God
could ever be your friend,
he's shouting from the heavens above,
he's there to help you through,
you'll see how he simply loves you;
truth is, just this, he simply loves you.



## 324 Kath Fathers

There is a place where I can go,
when I'm feeling lonely or afraid.
There is a place where I can go,
that is special to me.
There is a love that's kind and warm,
a love that will kiss and comfort me.
There is a place where I can go,
that is special to me.

*No one loves me like Jesus loves me,*
*in his arms I'm happy.*
*No one knows me like Jesus knows me,*
*no one knows like he knows.*
*No one loves like he loves,*
*he loves me.*

There is a secret place to go,
where somebody knows me very well.
There is a secret place to go,
where I can be me.
And there my loving Jesus smiles,
he opens his arms and welcomes me.
There is a secret place to go,
where I can be me.

*Oh Jesus,*
*no one loves me the way you love me,*
*in your arms I'm happy.*
*No one knows me the way you know me,*
*no one knows like you know.*
*No one loves like you love,*
*you love me.*



## 325 Paul Field

There is no one else like you,
there's no one else like me.
Each of us is special to God,
that's the way it's meant to be.
I'm special, you're special,
we're special, don't you see,
there is no one else like you,
there's no one else like me.
Black or white, short or tall,
good or bad, God loves us all.
Loud or quiet, fat or thin,
each of us is special to him.



## 326 Noel Richards

There is pow'r in the name of Jesus;
we believe in his name.
We have called on the name of Jesus;
we are saved! We are saved!
At his name the demons flee.
At his name captives are freed,
for there is no other name that is higher
than Jesus!

*Continued overleaf*

There is pow'r in the name of Jesus,
like a sword in our hands.
We declare in the name of Jesus
we shall stand! We shall stand!
At his name God's enemies
shall be crushed beneath our feet,
for there is no other name that is higher
than Jesus!



## 327 Capt. Alan Price, CA

There is so much to discover,
that God wants us to know.
There is so much to find out for
ourselves,
and that's the way to go.
When we learn what God has said,
when we act on what we've read,
there is so much to discover,
there's so much more to know.

There is so much to discover,
that God wants us to know.
There is so much to find out for
ourselves,
and that's the way to go.
Through the Spirit's pow'r within,
we can change the world for him.
There is so much to discover,
there's so much more to know.

There is so much to discover,
that God wants us to know.
There's so much to find out for
ourselves,
and that's the way to go.
If we're ever feeling bored,
we just need to ask the Lord
to show to us the things he's planned
for us to do,
and that's the way to go.



## 328 Capt. Alan Price, CA

There, on a cruel cross, for all to see;
killed like a criminal, how could it be?
That Jesus bore such pain and shame,
mock'd by those who only came
to stand and watch, yet still not see
what God was doing then, for you and me.

There, on a cruel cross, so painfully;
killed like a criminal, yet willingly.
Lord Jesus bore such pain and shame,
for that is why he really came;
the greatest act of history,
what God was doing then, for you and me.

Lord, I may never understand,
or know the reason why
the only way to be forgiv'n,
was that you should die;
I worship you; I follow you;
I live for you; I trust in you.



## 329 Unknown

There once was a man called Daniel
(good old Daniel),
and Daniel prayed three times a day
(good old Daniel);
but the king's decree said 'Worship me!'
(poor old Daniel),
but Daniel would not bend the knee!
(good old Daniel).
So the gates went 'crash' (crash),
and the locks went 'click' (click),
and the lions began to (roar),
and the lions began to (roar),
but they couldn't eat Daniel if they tried
(good old Daniel),
because the Lord was on his side (good
old Daniel).

## 330 Doug Horley and Vanessa Freeman

There's a King above the heavens,
there's a King above the earth,
and from out of timeless history,
he brought mankind to birth.
And when sin brought separation,
and tore the heart of the King,
he sent his son, Jesus Christ,
a sacrifice for sin.

*Hoop sah oh, oh, oh.*
*Hoop sah oh, oh, oh.*
*Hoop sah oh.*
*Hoop sah oh.*
(Repeat)

Let the rhythm move your spirit,
let the rhythm touch your soul.
It's the sound of love, the sound of life,
it's the sound of hope.
Let the truth be seen by people
as he is lifted high.
May nations turn, may nations find
the hope in Jesus Christ.

There's a cry rising up. (Lift him high.)
There's a cry rising up. (He's alive.)
There's a cry rising up. (Oh, oh, oh, it's
Jesus.)
*(Repeat)*

King of heaven,
King of heaven,
King of heaven, we lift you high.
*(Repeat)*



## 331 Ian Smale

There's nothing better than being a
soldier
in the army of the Lord.
There's nothing better than being a
soldier
in the army of the Lord.
We'll live by faith and not by sight,
not by power, not by might,
but by his Spirit win ev'ry fight.



## 332 Ian Smale

There's nothing I like better than to praise.
There's nothing I like better than to praise.
'Cos, Lord, I love you,
and there's nothing I would rather do
than whisper about it, talk all about it,
shout all about it all my days.



## 333 Roger Jones

There were ninety-nine sheep back safe
in the fold,
but one of them's left outside in the cold.
The shepherd was wond'ring,
'Oh where, tell me where can it be?
Can it be?
Where? Where? Where's the missing
one?
Where? Where? Where's the missing one?
Oh, where can it be?'

So the shepherd set out in dead of the
night,
the wind and the rain, a pitiful sight.
He kept right on searching,
but no sheep at all could he see!
Could he see!
Where? Where? Where's the missing one?
Where? Where? Where's the missing one?
Oh, where can it be?

*Continued overleaf*

But the shepherd, at last, he found his
lost sheep,
all ragged and cold and trying to sleep.
He picked it right up
and he carried it home. Now it's found!
Now it's found!
There! There! There's the missing one!
There! There! There's the missing one!
And now it is found!



## 334 Damian Lundy

The Spirit lives to set us free,
walk, walk in the light.
He binds us all in unity,
walk, walk in the light.

*Walk in the light,*
*walk in the light,*
*walk in the light,*
*walk in the light of the Lord.*

Jesus promised life to all,
walk, walk in the light.
The dead were wakened by his call,
walk, walk in the light.

He died in pain on Calvary,
walk, walk in the light,
to save the lost like you and me,
walk, walk in the light.

We know his death was not the end,
walk, walk in the light.
He gave his Spirit to be our friend,
walk, walk in the light.

The Spirit lives in you and me,
walk, walk in the light.
His light will shine for all to see,
walk, walk in the light.



## 335 Mick Gisbey

The time has come to have some fun,
don't stand alone, get with someone.
We're gonna have a party in this place.
Let the music fill the air,
let joy and laughter lift your cares,
we're gonna have a party in this place,
we're gonna have a party in this place.

*Time to be happy, let me hear you*
*shout:*
*dancing with friends, let your joy*
*break out.*
*Jesus is amongst us, he loves to see*
*you smile.*
*Leave your sadness and be happy for*
*a while,*
*happy for a while.*

Wave the banners, ribbons too:
God wants his joy to flow through you.
We're gonna have a party in this place.
Don't hold back or live in fear,
there's room for young and old ones here,
we're gonna have a party in this place,
we're gonna have a party in this place.



## 336 Unknown

The wise man built his house upon
the rock,
the wise man built his house upon
the rock,
the wise man built his house upon
the rock,
and the rain came tumbling down.
And the rain came down and the floods
came up,
the rain came down and the floods
came up,
the rain came down and the floods
came up,
and the house on the rock stood firm.

The foolish man built his house upon
the sand,
the foolish man built his house upon
the sand,
the foolish man built his house upon
the sand,
and the rain came tumbling down.
And the rain came down and the floods
came up,
the rain came down and the floods
came up,
the rain came down and the floods
came up,
and the house on the sand fell flat.



## 337 Paul Field

The women went to Jesus' tomb
on that Easter day,
they found an angel had been there
to roll the stone away.

*Roll the stone, roll the stone,*
*roll the stone away.*
*The angel came on Easter day*
*to roll the stone away.*

They found that Jesus was alive,
and still he lives today,
for God has raised him from the dead,
and rolled the stone away.

Don't let your heart be like a tomb,
empty, dark and grey,
trust in Jesus, he's the rock
to roll your stone away.

Last chorus
*Roll the stone, roll the stone,*
*roll the stone away.*
*Trust in Jesus, he's the rock*
*to roll your stone away.*
*Trust in Jesus, he's the rock*
*to roll your stone away.*



## 338 Capt. Alan Price, CA

The word of the Lord is planted in my
heart
and I want to see it grow.
The word of the Lord is planted in my
heart
and I want you to know,
I won't let the enemy take it,
or let bad times shake it;
I won't let other things choke it out
(choke, choke, choke),
'cos I want to let it grow, grow, grow,
'cos I want to let it grow!
(yeah!)



## 339 Capt. Alan Price, CA

This is a catchy songa, we sing it to the
conga,
we dance and sing to Christ the King.
Why don't you sing alonga, while we
dance the conga,
praise God above for all his love.

King David danced before the Lord,
worship filled his heart;
we can dance before him, too,
this is how we start . . .

Jesus is the greatest friend,
alive for us today,
he said, 'I'm with you 'till the end,
I'm with you all the way!'

## 340 Capt. Alan Price, CA

This is a song for the children of the Lord,
a simple song to our King.
A song of happiness and simple faith,
our praise and thanks we bring.

This is a dance for the children of the Lord,
a simple dance for our King.
A dance of happiness and simple faith,
our praise and thanks we bring.

Lai, lai, lai, . . .



## 341 Les Garrett

This is the day,
this is the day that the Lord has made,
that the Lord has made;
we shall rejoice,
we shall rejoice and be glad in it,
and be glad in it.
This is the day that the Lord has made,
we shall rejoice and be glad in it;
this is the day,
this is the day that the Lord has made.



## 342 Paul Field

This is the nose God chose for me,
and I suppose that you can see,
there's no one in the world with a nose
like me,
thank you, Lord.
*(Repeat)*

*Thank you, Lord,*
*because we know it's true,*
*all these diff'rent faces,*
*look beautiful to you.*

These are the ears God chose for me,
and I suppose that you can see,
there's no one in the world with ears
like me,
thank you, Lord.
*(Repeat)*

This is the mouth God chose for me,
and I suppose that you can see,
there's no one in the world with a mouth
like me,
thank you, Lord.
*(Repeat)*

These are the eyes God chose for me,
and I suppose that you can see,
there's no one in the world with eyes
like me,
thank you, Lord.
*(Repeat)*



## 343 Ernie Rettino and Debbie Kerner Rettino

This little light of mine, I'm gonna let it
shine.
This little light of mine, I'm gonna let it
shine.
This little light of mine, I'm gonna let it
shine.
Ev'ry day, ev'ry day, ev'ry day in ev'ry way.
I'm gonna let my little light shine.
*(Repeat)*

On a Monday, he gave me the gift of love.
On a Tuesday, his peace came down
from above.
On a Wednesday, he told me just what
to say.
On a Thursday, he told me just how to
pray.
On a Friday, he gave me a little more faith.

On a Saturday, he gave me a lot more grace.
On a Sunday, he gave me the power divine
to let my little light shine.



## 344 Capt. Alan Price, CA

Three little words that mean so much,
'God loves me!'
Three little words that deeply touch me,
'God loves me!'
I know it, 'cos God said it,
and he would never lie.
I know it, 'cos he showed it,
when he sent his Son to die for me.
Three little words that mean so much,
'God loves me!'

Three little words I mean so much, Lord,
'I love you!'
Three little words I want to tell you,
'I love you!'
You know that when I say it,
I'm trying to be real.
You know that when I say it,
it's not just when I feel you love me.
Three little words I want to tell you,
'I love you!'



## 345 C. C. Kerr

Two little eyes to look to God,
two little ears to hear his word,
two little feet to walk in his ways,
two little lips to sing his praise,
two little hands to do his will,
and one little heart to love him still.



## 346 Sammy Horner

*Uh well, it's excellent to be obedient, u-hu-hu!*
*Uh well, it's excellent to be obedient, u-hu-hu!*
*You don't say 'no' to your ma and pa; you say 'u-hu'.*

Uh well, it ain't real good to be real rude, no, no, no.
Uh well, it ain't real good to be real rude, no, no, no.
You've gotta treat your parents like you know you should, u-hu-hu!

It don't show aptitude to have an attitude, no, no, no.
It don't show aptitude to have an attitude, no, no, no.
You've gotta treat your parents like you know you should, u-hu-hu!



## 347 Paul Field

Up, down, turn around,
touch your head, touch the ground,
left, right, side to side,
legs together, legs astride,
stand up straight, touch your toes,
squeeze your tum, pinch your nose.
Up, down, turn around,
clap your hands and shout (all right!)
*(Repeat)*

Fit for life, in body and in mind.
Fit for life, to live for Jesus all the time.
Up, down, turn, around, clap your hands and shout (yeah!)

## 348 Capt. Alan Price, CA

*Up, up, up and away!*
*We're taking off as we follow Jesus.*
*Up, up, up and away!*
*We're moving on with God.*

Our luggage packed and our ticket in hand,
we come to Jesus and we understand
that he paid a great price, even willing to die.
When we know we're forgiven it's as if we can fly!

His Spirit's fuel gives the power we need
for ev'ry word, and for ev'ry deed,
and a beacon is there to guide us along,
his word is the Bible, shows what's right and what's wrong.



## 349 Jim Bailey

*We are kingdom kids, kids of the kingdom.*
*We let Jesus Christ be number one in our lives.*
*We are kingdom kids, kids of the kingdom.*
*We're gonna serve our God and King.*

Jesus Christ is alive, reigning with the Father,
we're gonna let his will be done on earth.
Putting Jesus first, for the Spirit of God we thirst,
singing to Jesus for all he's worth.

Whatever we do, Jesus it's for you,
we want you to completely be our Lord.
You came and gave your life, and so it's only right,
we should love you more and more.



## 350 Traditional South African. Translation (verse 1) Anders Nyberg, (verses 2 and 3) Andrew Maries

We are marching in the light of God,
we are marching in the light of God.
We are marching in the light of God,
we are marching in the light of God.

*We are marching, marching,*
*we are marching, oh,*
*we are marching in the light of God.*
(Repeat)

We are living in the love of God . . .

We are moving in the pow'r of God . . .

*Optional traditional South African words*

Siyahamb' ekukhanyen' kwenkhos',
siyahamb' ekukhanyen' kwenkhos'.
Siyahamb' ekukhanyen' kwenkhos',
siyahamb' ekukhanyen' kwenkhos'.

*Siyahamba, hamba,*
*siyahamba, hamba,*
*siyahamb' ekukhanyen' kwenkhos'.*
(Repeat)



## 351 Ian Smale

We are one, we are family together,
'cause we've one Father caring for us all.
We are one, we are related to each other;
Lord, help me to love my family much more.

## 352 Capt. Alan Price, CA

*We are the Lord's kids, his kids,*
*special kids, chosen kids,*
*big kids, little kids, following the Lord.*
(Repeat)

Though we may be small,
Jesus wants us all;
an army for the Lord,
living by his Word.
*(Repeat)*

However old we are,
we can know his pow'r;
whoever we may be,
Jesus is the key.
*(Repeat)*

The way we think, the way we act,
the enemy we'll fight!
At school, at home, at work, at play,
we'll learn to do what's right.
*(Repeat)*



## 353 Ian Smale

We believe in Hebrews thirteen, eight,
Jesus Christ is never out of date.
If it's yesterday or today, or for evermore,
Jesus stays the same and that is great.



## 354 Sammy Horner

We don't believe the devil's lie,
we will shout our battle cry.
Though we may be very small,
Jesus Christ is Lord of all.
He's good for me, he's good for you.
He's good for me, good for our whole
church.

When temptation comes our way,
this is what we're gonna say:
'Don't you come and mess with me,
in Jesus' name our victory.
In Jesus' name our victory.
In Jesus' name our victory.'

Jesus is the King of kings,
he's the Lord of ev'rything.
If Satan comes, here's what we say:
'In Jesus' name, now go away.
Now go away, in Jesus' name!
Now go away, in Jesus' name!
Now go away, in Jesus' name!'



## 355 Paul Crouch and David Mudie

We don't sing songs just for
ourselves,
we sing them for our King,
and if we really mean it,
then he loves it when we sing.

*So we clap our hands (clap),*
*stamp our feet (stamp),*
*jump up and down (boing boing),*
*touch our toes (oh!),*
*and sing them for our King,*
*sing them for our King,*
*sing them for our King,*
*sing them for our King.*

We don't sing songs to please our
friends,
we sing them for our King,
and if we really mean it,
then he loves it when we sing.

## 356 Geoffrey Gardner

Welcome, welcome,
we're glad that you have come;
welcome, welcome,
from each and ev'ry one.

Welcome, welcome,
we're glad that you belong;
welcome, welcome,
from each and ev'ry one.



## 357 Debby Kerner

Welcome to the family,
we're glad that you have come
to share your life with us,
as we grow in love;
and may we always be to you
what God would have us be,
a family always there,
to be strong and to lean on.
May we learn to love each other
more with each new day,
may words of love be on our lips
in ev'rything we say.
May the Spirit melt our hearts
and teach us how to pray,
that we might be a true family.



## 358 Capt. Alan Price, CA

We'll sing this song for you,
a birthday song for you,
we'll sing this song for you today.
May Jesus be with you
in ev'rything you do,
this is our birthday pray'r
for you today.
*(Repeat)*

Happy birthday! Happy birthday!
Happy birthday to you!



## 359 Capt. Alan Price, CA

*We need to grow, grow, grow, grow,*
*grow in the grace of the Saviour,*
*we need to grow, grow, grow, grow,*
*grow in the knowledge of Jesus our Lord.**
(Repeat)

We'll grow as we pray to him,
spend some time each day.
We'll grow as we worship him,
give him our love and praise!

We grow as we read of him
and the way for us to live;
we'll grow as we work for him,
as our lives to him we give.

We grow as we learn and share
with others that we know;
these are the things to do
if we really want to grow.

* Last time
*We need to grow in the knowledge of Jesus our Lord.*



## 360 Capt. Alan Price, CA

We praise God in the morning when the sun is bright,
we praise him in the evening when day turns to night.
We praise him if it's sunny or if it's wet.
No matter what the weather we'll never forget to

*praise God (bop, bop, showaddy do wah).*
*Praise God (bop, bop, showaddy do wah).*
*Hallelujah, we'll praise the Lord.*

We praise God when we're singing our songs of praise,
we praise him when we worship in our different ways,
we praise him for the food that we eat each day,
but in everything we do we want to say,



## 361 Capt. Alan Price, CA

We praise you, Jesus, we praise you, Jesus,
we just want to let you know.
We praise you, Jesus, we praise you, Jesus,
when you came so long ago.
You came to save us,
new life you gave us,
when you died upon the cross.
And that's the reason that we're believin'
that you really care for us!



## 362 Capt. Alan Price, CA

We're a bright light together,
with the light of Jesus we shine;
we're a grand band together,
with our friend Jesus it's fine.
We're a swell smell together,
it's the fragrance of Jesus we share!
Whenever we are together,
Jesus is specially there.
Even before time began,
we were part of God's great plan;
'cos of Jesus we would be
part of his great family!



## 363 Capt. Alan Price, CA

We're going to praise the Lord,
we're going to praise the Lord,
we're going to praise the Lord,
for he is good!
We're going to praise the Lord,
we're going to praise the Lord,
we're going to praise the Lord,
for he is good!

We'll praise him with our shouts of praise
(oggie, oggie, oggie, oy, oy, oy);
we'll praise him in more normal ways
(hallelujah! hallelu);
we'll praise him by the way we live
(stand up, stand up for Jesus);
we'll praise him in the way we give
(time and money, time and money).
More than anything else we do,
Lord, we give our praise to you!



## 364 Andrew and Pauline Pearson

We wanna sing about your love
and tell ev'ryone we know.
Let it change our lives
so that we can let it show.
Father, we receive your love
that comes from knowing you,
as we enjoy your love,
help us show love to others too.

*Let your love pour into our lives, O Lord,*
*let your love pour into our lives.*
*Let your love pour into our lives, O Lord,*
*let your love pour into our lives.*

*Continued overleaf*

We wanna sing about your love
and tell ev'ryone we know.
Let it change our lives
so that we can let it show.
Jesus we receive the joy
that comes from knowing you.
The way you gave your life,
help us to offer ours to you.

*Let your joy pour into our lives,*
*O Lord,*
*let your joy pour into our lives.*
*Let your joy pour into our lives,*
*O Lord,*
*let your joy pour into our lives.*

We wanna sing about your love
and tell ev'ryone we know.
Let it change our lives
so that we can let it show.
Spirit we receive the pow'r
that comes from knowing you.
Will you change our lives,
so we can be of use to you?

*Let your power pour into our lives . . .*



## 365 Doug Horley

We want to see Jesus lifted high,
a banner that flies across this land,
that all men might see the truth
and know he is the way to heaven.
*(Repeat)*

*We want to see, we want to see,*
*we want to see Jesus lifted high.*
*We want to see, we want to see,*
*we want to see Jesus lifted high.*

Step by step we're moving forward,
little by little taking ground,
ev'ry prayer a powerful weapon,
strongholds come tumbling down,
and down, and down, and down.

We want to see Jesus . . .

*We're gonna see . . .*



## 366 Kath Hall

*We will turn the hearts of the fathers*
*so they will look again to their children.*
*We will turn the hearts of the children*
*so that together we can look to you.*
(Repeat)

The young and the old now,
standing together,
looking to Jesus to carry us through.
All diff'rent races, all diff'rent ages,
all of us here for your glory.
And we call on your Spirit,
keep us together and pour in your power.

The walls have been broken,
we stand as one now,
one in the Spirit and won by your blood.
We're moving forwards under your banner,
telling the world of your glory.
And we take on your promise,
together we'll welcome the Day of
the Lord!



## 367 Capt. Alan Price, CA

*We worship you, Father, Son and Holy*
*Spirit;*
*believe in you, Holy Trinity.*
*We follow you, Father, Son and Holy*
*Spirit;*
*Almighty God, Holy Trinity.*

God the Father, God the Son,
and Holy Spirit too;
each is God, yet God is One,
the Bible says it's true.

I don't pretend to understand
how this can really be,
yet by faith I know it's true,
this holy mystery.



## 368 Mick Gisbey

What a whale of a tale when Jonah sailed
out on the ocean blue:
God spoke that day, but he ran away
from what he was told to do;
and out on a boat that could hardly float,
on a rough and stormy sea,
the sailors asked: 'Whose fault is this?'
and Jonah piped up: 'Me!'

It doesn't pay to disobey,
for what God said is right;
don't try to hide, God sees inside
so don't put up a fight.
*(Repeat)*



## 369 Lucy East

*All* What noise shall we make to say
that God is great?
What noise shall we make unto
the Lord?
*Leader* Let's make a loud noise to say
that God is great.
Let's make a loud noise unto the
Lord.
*All* Here is my loud noise:
Here is my loud noise:
Here is my loud noise unto the
Lord.

Let's make a quiet noise . . .

Let's make a fast noise . . .

Let's make a slow noise . . .

Let's make a joyful noise . . .

Let's make a praising noise . . .
Here is my praising noise: God is good!

We love making noise
to say that God is great.
We love making noise
unto the Lord.



## 370 Mary Wright

What was it like for the shepherds,
out on the hills in the night?
What was it like for the shepherds,
on seeing the bright, shining light?

(Shout) *Hear the angels!*

*Glory! Glory! Glory to God on high!*
*Glory! Glory! Glory to God on high!*

What was it like for the shepherds,
seeing an angel out there?
What was it like for the shepherds,
so scared by the sudden bright glare?

What was it like for the shepherds,
leaving their sheep in the cold?
What was it like for the shepherds
to do as the angel had told?

There was great joy for the shepherds,
leaving their fields cold and wild!
There was great joy for the shepherds,
on seeing the newly born child.

## 371 Jan Struther

When a knight won his spurs, in the stories of old,
he was gentle and brave he was gallant and bold;
with a shield on his arm and a lance in his hand,
for God and for valour he rode through the land.

No charger have I, and no sword by my side,
yet still to adventure and battle I ride,
though back into storyland giants have fled,
and the knights are no more and the dragons are dead.

Let faith be my shield and let joy be my steed
'gainst the dragons of anger, the ogres of greed;
and let me set free, with the sword of my youth
for the castle of darkness, the pow'r of the truth.



## 372 Capt. Alan Price, CA

Whenever I'm afraid, I will trust in Jesus,
whenever I'm afraid, I will trust in him.
Whenever I'm afraid, I will trust in Jesus,
whenever I'm afraid, I will trust in him.

When I'm alone, I know he's there,
when it's dark, I know he's near,
when I am hurt, I know he cares,
I know he's bigger than all my fears.



## 373 Capt. Alan Price, CA

When I am hurt in the daily fight
to live for Jesus and do what is right,
I'll find a quiet place, and then I'll pray
and ask God to heal what's been damaged that day.

I'll ask his forgiveness for things I've done wrong,
and breathe in his Spirit once more to be strong;
and so I'll be ready to face a new day,
with ev'ry new challenge that may come my way.



## 374 Rosie Jarvis

When I look at the trees,
blowing in the breeze,
oo, I praise you,
oo, I praise you.
When I see a bird up high,
swooping in the sky,
oo, I praise you,
oo, I praise you.

*It's a wonderful world for boys and girls,*
*such a wonderful world for boys and girls,*
*and we praise you, Creator God.*

When I feel the gentle rain,
splashing down again,
oo, I praise you,
oo, I praise you.
When I touch the golden sand,
spreading it with my hand,
oo, I praise you,
oo, I praise you.

When I see the silver stars,
sparkling in the skies,
oo, I praise you,
oo, I praise you.



## 375 Dave Bird and Sarah Lacy

When I'm in bed and it's night,
I don't want mum to turn out the light,
because there might be giants or things
that frighten, or monsters looking at me.
But when I'm shaking down to my
knees,
seeing the shadows up in the trees,
I will remember you are my friend
and I will be fine, just listen to me!

*'Cause I've got a friend who's bigger
than that,
he never leaves me whatever I'm at;
there is no need for fear 'cause you
are here,
oh Jesus, you're all that I need.
Whenever I call you, you're already here,
and you always listen whatever my fear,
and I want to know you more and now
I'm sure that friends for ever we'll be.*

There's a boy in the class above me,
and he's so much bigger than me,
and I don't want to go to the
playground,
'cause I'm scared of what he'd do to me!

*But I've got a friend . . .*

And when I'm feeling sad and alone,
and all the other kids have gone home,
then I can pray and call out your name
and I'll know that you are with me once
more.

*And I've got a friend . . .*



## 376 Mark and Helen Johnson

When I think about the cross,
when I think of Jesus,
I'm reminded of his love,
love that never leaves me.
Who am I that he should die,
giving life so freely?
*(Repeat)*

*Last time*
When I think about the cross,
help me to believe it.



## 377 Nigel Hemming

When there is nowhere to turn,
when there is no one who cares,
when I am feeling afraid and alone,
my Jesus will always be there.

I know I'm his precious child.
I know he's my special friend.
I know that I'll always be safe in his love,
as I give him my heart once again.



## 378 Joe King

When there's hard times or there's good
times,
when the rain falls or the sun shines,
when you test me or you bless me,
my resolve will none the less be:

*I will love you come what may,
I will love you ev'ry day;
I will love you now and for evermore.*

*Continued overleaf*

When there's dark clouds or there's clear skies,
when it's sunset or it's sunrise,
when I'm needy or I've plenty,
Lord, not one thing will prevent me:

*I will love you come what may,*
*I will love you ev'ry day;*
*I will love you now and for evermore.*

When your presence seems so distant,
when my doubts seem so persistent,
then no matter how I'm feeling,
Lord, in one thing I'm unyielding:

When the battle seems so endless,
when I'm feeling so defenceless,
when the enemy surrounds me
and his arrows fly around me:

When my future is uncertain,
when my heart is heavy-burdened,
when I'm tired or I'm hurting,
Lord, in one thing I'm determined:

When the past seems to pursue me,
when temptation whispers to me,
when my worst fears are awakened,
Lord, on one thing I'm unshaken:



## 379 Capt. Alan Price, CA

When the time is right,
whether day or night,
the Lord Jesus Christ will come again
(he'll come again).
As we wait for that day,
in our work and our play,
we'll let our light shine bright
and live for the King who will reign.



## 380 Capt. Alan Price, CA

When we're together with Jesus
and we happily sing his songs,
it's easy to be his follower,
it's good to know we belong;
but at other times it can be so hard
to do what's right and good.
When those around don't know the Lord,
and don't live as they should.
O Lord, keep me strong,
never to deny you.
O Lord, when it's hard,
help me to keep by you.



## 381 Mike Burn

When you pray, go into your own room;
when you pray, close the door.
*(Repeat)*

Pray to Father, who is unseen,
and your Father, who sees what you do,
he'll reward you.

When you pray, don't use lots of long words,
when you pray, as some people do.
They think if their prayers go on for ages,
God will hear, but that isn't true.

For your Father already knows,
yes, your Father, he knows what you need
and will answer.

## 382 Paul Field and Ralph Chambers

When you're feeling good, put your
thumbs up.
When you're feeling bad, put them down.
When you're feeling happy you can smile
all day.
When you're feeling low, wear a frown;
but don't just follow your feelings,
trust in God and his Word.
No matter what you feel, put your
thumbs up,
put your faith in the Lord.



## 383 Capt. Alan Price, CA

Wherever he rules, it's good when he is
in charge,
it's best when we do as he says,
it pleases God:
let Jesus Christ be 'Number One' in our
lives.
*(Repeat)*

For the Son of God is the King of
hearts,
who rules with love, truth and justice;
and we will speak his words and do his
deeds,
by the pow'r of the Spirit he gives us!

Wherever he rules, it's good when he is
in charge,
it's best when we do as he says, it
pleases God:
let Jesus Christ be 'Number One' in our
lives.
Let Jesus Christ be 'Number One',
Jesus Christ be 'Number One',
Jesus Christ be 'Number One' in our
lives!



## 384 Graham Kendrick

Whether you're one or whether you're two
or three or four or five,
six or sev'n or eight or nine,
it's good to be alive.
It really doesn't matter how old you are,
Jesus loves you whoever you are.

*La la la la la la la la, la,*
*Jesus loves us all.*
*La la la la la la la la, la,*
*Jesus loves us all.*

Whether you're big or whether you're
small,
or somewhere in between,
first in the class or middle or last,
we're all the same to him.
It really doesn't matter how clever you are,
Jesus loves you whoever you are.



## 385 Unknown

Who made the twinkling stars,
the twinkling stars, the twinkling stars?
Who made the twinkling stars?
Our Father God.

Who made the birds that fly,
the birds that fly, the birds that fly?
Who made the birds that fly?
Our Father God.

Who made the rolling seas,
the rolling seas, the rolling seas?
Who made the rolling seas?
Our Father God.

Who made both you and me,
you and me, you and me?
Who made both you and me?
Our Father God.

## 386 Paul Booth

Who put the colours in the rainbow?
Who put the salt into the sea?
Who put the cold into the snowflake?
Who made you and me?
Who put the hump upon the camel?
Who put the neck on the giraffe?
Who put the tail upon the monkey?
Who made hyenas laugh?
Who made whales and snails and quails?
Who made hogs and dogs and frogs?
Who made bats and rats and cats?
Who made ev'rything?

Who put the gold into the sunshine?
Who put the sparkle in the stars?
Who put the silver in the moonlight?
Who made Earth and Mars?
Who put the scent into the roses?
Who taught the honey bees to dance?
Who put the tree inside the acorn?
It surely can't be chance!
Who made seas and leaves and trees?
Who made snow and winds that blow?
Who made streams and rivers flow?
God made all of these!



## 387 Mark and Helen Johnson

Who spoke words of wisdom and life?
Only the one they call Jesus.
Understood what people are like?
Nobody other than him.
Who performed miraculous signs?
Only the one they call Jesus.
Healed the sick, gave sight to the blind?
Nobody other than him.

*Hosanna! Hosanna!*
*Praise him! Come praise him!*
*Hosanna! Hosanna!*
*Lift up your voices and sing!*

Who took children into his arms?
Only the one they call Jesus.
Spoke to storms and made them calm?
Nobody other than him.
Who raised Lazarus from the dead?
Only the one they call Jesus.
Made a feast of fishes and bread?
Nobody other than him.

Who made friends with people
  despised?
Only the one they call Jesus.
Turned the water into good wine?
Nobody other than him.
Who got people following him?
Only the one they call Jesus.
Changed their lives, forgave all their sin?
Nobody other than him.



## 388 Unknown

Who's the king of the jungle?
Who's the king of the sea?
Who's the king of the universe,
and who's the king of me?
I'll tell you: J - E - S - U - S is,
he's the king of me;
he's the king of the universe,
the jungle and the sea.

## 389 Paul Herbert

Who taught the spider to spin his web?
Who spoke the first words ever said?
Who put the waves in the deep blue sea?
Who knows all there is about me, me, me?
My Father.

*My Father is big, he's strong and he's tough,*
*I know that he cares, his word I trust.*
*Whenever I fall, he helps me to stand.*
*My Father holds me secure in his hand.*

Who taught the bird to sing her song?
Who drew the line between right and wrong?
Who paints the rainbow across the sky?
Who will hear me when I cry, cry, cry?
My Father.



## 390 Capt. Alan Price, CA

*Why is it me? Why is it me?*
*Why do all the things like this happen to me?*
*Why is it me? Why is it me?*
*Isn't there someone else other than me?*

Ananias heard the Lord call him one day,
'I've got a job for you to do straight away.
Find a house in Straight Street and ask for a man,
his name is Saul of Tarsus, now be quick as you can.'

'This Saul had a vision and it's going to come true,
he's seen a man lay hands on him, and that man is you!'
Ananais was worried, 'cos he'd heard about Saul,
he'd caused trouble for believers – he wasn't nice at all!
Oh . . .

God said, 'Go, Ananias, and do what I ask,
I've chosen this Saul for a special task.'
Ananias knew that he had to obey,
he knew that he could trust the Lord, come what may.
But . . .

He went and found the house and laid his hands on Saul,
the Holy Spirit came with power – it didn't hurt at all.
God asks hard things even now – and of children too.
Don't miss the adventure, it could happen to you!
Oh . . .

Last Chorus
*Could it be me? Could it be me?*
*How could anything like this happen to me?*
*Could it be me? Could it be me?*
*Though there may be someone else, it could be me.*



## 391 Tim Moyler and the children of ICHTHUS, Beckenham

*You are the best,*
*better than all the rest;*
*Jesus you're the best.*
*You are the best,*
*better than all the rest;*
*Jesus you're the best.*

Thank you, Lord, for giving us
our food and drink each day.
When we're sick you heal us with your love.
Lord, we love to praise you,
for you love and care for us.
We want to get to know you more each day.

## 392 Chris Jackson

You are the Light of the world,
I won't walk in darkness.
You are the Way, the Truth and the Life,
I'm gonna follow you.

You are the good, Good Shepherd,
you take care of me.
You are the Resurrection and the Life,
I'm gonna live with you.

You are the Bread of Life,
I will not be hungry.
You are the Vine and I am the branch,
I will abide in you.

You are the great I AM,
who was and is and is to come.



## 393 Ralph Chambers

You can't catch a plane to take you to heaven,
not even a spaceship can get that far.
You can't take a hovercraft or helicopter journey,
or drive in the fastest racing car.
Only Jesus, only Jesus, only Jesus is the way.
Only Jesus, only Jesus, only Jesus is the way.



## 394 Bev Gammon

*You give me joy, such a bubbly joy*
*that no one else can give me.*
*You give me joy, such a bubbly joy*
*that no one else can give me.*

I want to dance and run around,
I want to shout your name out loud,
'cos you give me joy, such a bubbly joy
that no one else can give me.

I want to laugh and clap my hands,
I want to praise you through the land,
'cos you give me joy, such a bubbly joy
that no one else can give me.



## 395 Capt. Alan Price, CA

You lift your left arm high, your left arm high,
your left arm straight up, wave it in the sky.
You raise your arm to Jesus as you sing God's praise,
it's the Holy Hokey for God!

*Give the glory to the Father,*
*give the glory to the Son,*
*give the glory to the Spirit,*
*our great God 'Three in One'*
*Amen!*

You lift your right arm high, your right arm high,
your right arm straight up, wave it in the sky.
You raise your arm to Jesus as you sing God's praise,
it's the Holy Hokey for God!

You lift your left arm high, your right arm high,
both arms straight up, wave them in the sky.
You raise your arms to Jesus as you sing God's praise,
it's the Holy Hokey for God!

You lift your face up high, your face up high,
lift your face up, gazing to the sky.
You're looking up to Jesus as you sing God's praise,
it's the Holy Hokey for God!



## 396 Mark and Helen Johnson

You may be happy, you may be sad,
you may be pretty or plain;
you may be skinny or getting fat,
maybe you wish you could change.

You may be wealthy, you may be poor,
you may be scruffy or smart;
but love is real when you know for sure,
it takes you just as you are.

*If we're right or we're wrong,*
*if we're weak or we're strong,*
*if we're winning or losing a game;*
*whether black or white skin,*
*with a frown or a grin,*
*well, the Lord loves us all just the same.*

They say to copy the TV stars,
they say 'Keep up with the trends';
to have the fashions and look the part,
just like the rest of your friends.

They say 'Try harder', they say 'Perform',
they say 'Do things to impress';
but love is real when you know for sure,
it won't depend on success.



## 397 Mick Gisbey

You may think I'm so young, too young to understand;
don't forget, in God's eyes, he looks on me as grand.
He never, never limits the giant that's in me;
he leads me through my childhood, supernaturally.

I'm not a grasshopper, I'm a giant in the Lord.
I'm not a grasshopper, I'm a giant in the Lord.
*(Repeat)*



## 398 Ian Smale

You never put a light under a dirty old bucket.
You never put your light under a dirty old bucket.
You never put your light under a dirty old bucket
if you want light to shine around, round, round.
Shine, shine around, round, round.
Shine, shine around, round, round.
Shine a light that ev'ryone can see.
Lord, help me let my little light shine,
not just Sundays, all the time,
so friends give praise to you when they see me.

## 399 Ian White

Your name is Jesus, your love is true;
you ask your children to come to you,
to learn to follow, your Spirit's ways,
and with our whole lives bring you
praise.



## 400 Ian White

*You say the harvest is plentiful,*
*but workers are few,*
*Lord, I am ready and willing*
*just to follow you.*
(Repeat)

I'll listen and I'll pray
for what your Spirit says,
and I'll begin to look
inside your Holy Book.

I'll stay here in my street,
I'll tell the people I meet,
about Lord Jesus Christ,
who set me free inside.

I'll go to Africa,
I'll go to India,
wherever you send me,
that's where I want to be.

# Key Word Index

*The key word categories appear alphabetically and are cross-referenced to make it as easy as possible for worship leaders to find songs and hymns suitable for various themes and occasions.*

**FORGIVENESS**


See **Repentance and Forgiveness**


**GIFTS**


See **Holy Spirit – Gifts**


**GOD – FAITHFULNESS**



**GOD – GLORY**



**GOD – GOODNESS**



**GOD – GRACE**



**GOD – HOLINESS**



**GOD – MERCY**

**ESUS – RESURRECTION**



**ESUS – SAVIOUR**



**ESUS – SECOND COMING**



**OY**



**JUSTICE**



**KINGDOM**

See **Jesus – Kingdom**

**LOVE – GOD'S LOVE**

**LOVE – OUR LOVE FOR GOD**



**LOVE – OUR LOVE FOR OTHERS**



**MOTHER'S DAY**



**PEACE**



**PENTECOST**



**POWER**



**PRAISE**

**SPIRITUAL WARFARE**



**TEMPTATION**



**THANKSGIVING**



**TRINITY**

See **God – the Trinity**

**TROUBLES**



**UNITY**

See **Church**

**WITNESSING**

See **Evangelism**

**WORSHIP**

# Index of First Lines and Titles

*This index gives the first line of each hymn. If a hymn is known by an alternative title, this is also given, but indented and in italics.*

**U**



**W**



**Y**



**Z**

# Acknowledgements

The publishers wish to express their gratitude to the following for permission to include copyright material in this publication. Details of copyright owners are given underneath each individual hymn.

Robyn Barnett, 4 Heathcote Road, Twickenham, Middlesex, TW1 1RX.

CopyCare Ltd, PO Box 77, Hailsham, East Sussex, BN27 3EF, UK, on behalf of Mission Hills Music, Alliance Media Ltd, Word Music, Maranatha! Music, Mercy/Vineyard Publishing/Music Services, Chris Falson Music, CN Publishing, Whole World Publishing, Rettino Kerner Publishing, Zondervan Corporation/Brentwood Benson Music Publishing Inc, and CA Music/Music Services. Used by permission.

Daybreak Music, Silverdale Road, Eastbourne, East Sussex, BN20 7AB.

John Hardwick, 12 Normanton Way, Histon, Cambridgeshire, CB4 9XS.

Paul Herbert, 79 Bramford Road, Ipswich, Suffolk, IP1 2LT.

Ice Music Ltd, Bayley's Plantation, St Philip, Barbados, W. Indies.

Iona Community, Community House, Pearce Institute, Govan, Glasgow, G51 3UU.

IQ Music Ltd, Commercial House, 52 Perrymount Road, Haywards Heath, West Sussex, RH16 3DT.

Jubilate Hymns, 4 Thorne Park Road, Chelston, Torquay, TQ2 6RX.

Kingsway's Thankyou Music, PO Box 75, Eastbourne, East Sussex, BN23 6NW, UK, on behalf of Kingsway's Thankyou Music, Celebration (Europe and British Commonwealth, excl. Canada, Australasia and Africa), Little Misty Music (Worldwide, excl. Australia and New Zealand), Integrity's Hosanna! Music, Arise Ministries (Europe and British Commonwealth, excl. Australasia and Canada), Curious? Music UK (Worldwide, excl. USA), Glorie Music (Worldwide, excl. North America), Sound Truth Publishing (Europe and British Commonwealth, excl. Canada), Darlene Zschech/Hillsongs, Scripture in Song, a division of Integrity Music (UK only), and the songs of Ian Smale (Worldwide, excl. USA and Canada). Used by permission.

Leosong Copyright Service Ltd, Independent House, 54 Larkshall Road, Chingford, London, E4 6PD.

Make Way Music, PO Box 263, Croydon, Surrey, CR9 5AP. International copyright secured. All rights reserved. Used by permission.

Music Sales, 8/9 Frith Street, London, W1V 5TZ. All rights reserved. International copyright secured.

OCP Publications, 5536 NE Hassalo, Portland, OR 97213, USA. All rights reserved. Used by permission.

Oxford University Press, Great Clarendon Street, Oxford, OX2 6DP, from *Enlarged Songs of Praise,* 1931.

Powerpack/Learning Curve Music, PO Box 421, Hailsham, East Sussex, BN27 4ZA.

Scripture Union, 207-209 Queensway, Bletchley, Milton Keynes, Buckinghamshire, MK2 2EB.

Sea Dream Music, Sandcastle Productions, PO Box 13533, London, E7 0SG.

Sovereign Music UK, PO Box 356, Leighton Buzzard, Bedfordshire, LU7 8WP.

Sovereign Lifestyle Music, PO Box 356, Leighton Buzzard, Bedfordshire, LU7 8WP.

Stainer & Bell Ltd, PO Box 110, Victoria House, 23 Gruneisen Road, Finchley, London, N3 1DZ.

Wellingborough Christian Centre, St John Street, Wellingborough, Northants, NN8 4LG.

Windswept Pacific Music Ltd, Hope House, 40 St Peter's Road, London, W6.

Every effort has been made to trace the owners of copyright material and we hope that no copyright has been infringed. Pardon is sought and apology made if the contrary be the case, and a correction will be made in any reprint of this book.